# THE SCRIBNER
# RADIO MUSIC LIBRARY

VOLUME IX

*Compiled and Edited by*

JOHN TASKER HOWARD

SUPPLEMENTARY
COMPOSITIONS

PIANO *and* VOCAL

NEW YORK

CHARLES SCRIBNER'S SONS

# THE SCRIBNER RADIO MUSIC LIBRARY

## VOLUME IX — SUPPLEMENTARY COMPOSITIONS

## TABLE OF CONTENTS — TITLES

### STANDARD PIANO COMPOSITIONS

PASTORALE IN E MINOR . . . . . . Scarlatti, D. . . . . 6
FANTASIE NO. 3, IN D MINOR . . . Mozart, W. A. . . . . 9
RONDO IN C, OP. 51, NO. 1 . . . . Beethoven, L. Van . . 14
POLONAISE IN A (MILITARY), OP. 40,
  NO. 1 . . . . . . . . . . . . . Chopin, F. . . . . . 21
ROMANCE IN F SHARP, OP. 28, NO. 2 Schumann, R. . . . 28
BERCEUSE (CRADLE SONG) . . . . . Gottschalk, L. M. . . 30
ROMEO AND JULIET, (FANTASY OVER-
  TURE) (SELECTION) . . . . . . . Tschaikowsky, P. I. . 36
CONCERTO NO. 1, IN B FLAT MINOR,
  OP. 23 (SELECTION) . . . . . . . Tschaikowsky, P. I. . 41
NOCTURNE (PETITE SUITE) . . . . . Borodin, A. . . . . 48
PRELUDE, OP. 9, NO. 1 . . . . . . Scriabin, A. . . . . 50
NOCTURNE, OP. 9, NO. 2 . . . . . . Scriabin, A. . . . . 52
ORIENTALE, OP. 50, NO. 9 . . . . . Cui, C. . . . . . . 56
A.D. MDCXX (SEA PIECES), OP. 55,
  NO. 3 . . . . . . . . . . . . . MacDowell, E. . . . 59
FROM AN INDIAN LODGE (WOODLAND
  SKETCHES), OP. 51, NO. 5 . . . . MacDowell, E. . . . 62
PAVANE . . . . . . . . . . . . . Ravel, M. . . . . . 64
PETER AND THE WOLF (MUSICAL
  FAIRY TALE) (SELECTION) . . . . Prokofieff, S. . . . 69
PRELUDE IN E FLAT, OP. 34, NO. 19 Shostakovitch, D. . . 74

### EXCERPTS FROM BALLETS

PRELUDE TO THE AFTERNOON OF A
  FAUN . . . . . . . . . . . . . Debussy, C. . . . . 76
THE FIREBIRD . . . . . . . . . . Stravinsky, I. . . . 81

### EXCERPTS FROM GRAND OPERAS

RUSSLAN AND LUDMILLA . . . . . . Glinka, M. . . . . . 86
TRISTAN AND ISOLDA . . . . . . . Wagner, R. . . . . . 92
THE VALKYRIES . . . . . . . . . . Wagner, R. . . . . . 98

### EXCERPTS FROM LIGHT OPERA

THE BELLE OF NEW YORK . . . Kerker, G. . . . . . 102

### LIGHT PIANO COMPOSITIONS

IL BACIO (THE KISS) . . . . . . . Arditi, L. . . . . . 110
LA SERENATA, OP. 3 . . . . . . . Herbert, Victor . . 115
BROOKLYN BARCAROLLE . . . . . . Duke, Vernon . . . 118
MOZART MATRICULATES . . . . . . Templeton, Alec . . 120
A LULLABY . . . . . . . . . . . . Templeton, Alec . . 122
HANDFUL OF KEYS . . . . . . . Waller, Thomas (Fats) 125

### MODERN DANCE MUSIC

LA CUMPARSITA (TANGO) . . . . . Rodriguez, M. . . . 132
ADIOS (RHUMBA) . . . . . . . . . Madriguera, E. . . . 136

AMOR (BOLERO) . . . . . . . . Ruiz, G. . . . . . . 139
TICO-TICO (SAMBA) . . . . . . . . . Abreu, Z. . . . . . 142

### SACRED MUSIC FOR THE PIANO

CUJUS ANIMAM (STABAT MATER) . . Rossini, G. . . . . 146
STILL WATERS . . . . . . . . . . Howard, J. T. . . . 152
AT THE CONVENT (PETITE SUITE) . Borodin, A. . . . . 154

### SACRED SONGS

JESU, JOY OF MAN'S DESIRING . . . Bach, J. S. . . . . 157
AVE MARIA . . . . . . . . . . . . Schubert, F. . . . . 162
PANIS ANGELICUS (MESSE SOLEN-
  NELLE) . . . . . . . . . . . . . Franck, César . . . 168
AGNUS DEI . . . . . . . . . . . . Bizet, G. . . . . . 172

### HYMNS

O SACRED HEAD . . . . . . . . . Hassler, H. L. . . . 175
JESUS, MY LORD, MY GOD, MY ALL . Traditional . . . . 176
HOLY GOD, WE PRAISE THY NAME . Traditional . . . . 177
REJOICE, YE PURE IN HEART . . . Messiter, A. H. . . . 178
STAND UP FOR JESUS . . . . . . . Webb, G. J. . . . . 178
SAVIOUR, AGAIN TO THY DEAR NAME Hopkins, E. J. . . . 179
ETERNAL FATHER, STRONG TO SAVE . Dykes, J. B. . . . . 180
THE OLD RUGGED CROSS . . . . . Bennard, George . . 181

### CONCERT SONGS

THE TWO GRENADIERS . . . . . . Schumann, R. . . . 182
ALLERSEELEN (ALL SOULS' DAY) . . Strauss, R. . . . . 188
OL' DARKIE, OL' MULE . . . . . . Waring, Tom . . . 191
ABRAHAM . . . . . . . . . . . . MacGimsey, R. . . . 194
MISTAH SHAKESPEAH . . . . . . . Cadman, C. W. . . . 196
FOREVER AND A DAY . . . . . . . Hadley, H. K. . . . 200
INVICTUS . . . . . . . . . . . . Huhn, Bruno . . . . 204
SERENADE (GOOD NIGHT! GOOD
NIGHT, BELOVED!) . . . . . . . . Nevin, E. W. . . . . 208
GROW OLD ALONG WITH ME . . . Mana-Zucca . . . . 212
MARCHETA . . . . . . . . . . . . Schertzinger, V. L. . 214
A LITTLE BIT OF HEAVEN . . . . . Ball, E. R. . . . . . 216

### BALLADS AND FOLK-SONGS

AFTER THE BALL . . . . . . . . . Harris, C. K. . . . 219
HOME ON THE RANGE (COWBOY SONG) Traditional . . . 222
WHOOPEE TI YI YO (COWBOY SONG) Traditional . . . 223
TAKE ME BACK TO MY BOOTS AND
  SADDLE . . . . . . . . . . . . Samuels, W. G., L.
                                  Whitcup and T. Powell 224
DEEP IN THE HEART OF TEXAS . . . Swander, Don . . . 226
YOU ARE MY SUNSHINE . . . . . . Davis, J., and C.
                                  Mitchell . . . . 228

## PLANTATION AND MINSTREL SONGS

| | | |
|---|---|---|
| Buffalo Gals | *White, Cool* | 229 |
| Carry Me Back to Old Virginny | *Bland, J. A.* | 230 |
| Waiting for the Robert E. Lee | *Muir, L. F., and L. W. Gilbert* | 231 |
| Lazybones | *Mercer, J., and H. Carmichael* | 234 |

## PATRIOTIC SONGS

| | | |
|---|---|---|
| America the Beautiful | *Ward, S. A., and K. L. Bates* | 236 |
| The American Hymn | *Keller, M.* | 237 |
| The Caissons Go Rolling Along (Artillery Song) | *Gruber, E. L.* | 238 |
| The Marines' Hymn | *Traditional* | 240 |

# TABLE OF CONTENTS — COMPOSERS

| | | |
|---|---|---|
| *ABREU, ZEQUINHA* | Tico-Tico (Samba) | 142 |
| *ARDITI, LUIGI* | Il Bacio (The Kiss) | 110 |
| *BACH, J. S.* | Jesu, Joy of Man's Desiring | 157 |
| *BALL, ERNEST R.* | A Little Bit of Heaven | 216 |
| *BEETHOVEN, L. VAN* | Rondo in C, Op. 51, No. 1 | 14 |
| *BENNARD, REV. GEORGE* | The Old Rugged Cross | 181 |
| *BIZET, GEORGES* | Agnus Dei | 172 |
| *BLAND, JAMES A.* | Carry Me Back to Old Virginny | 230 |
| *BORODIN, ALEXANDER* | At the Convent (Petite Suite) | 154 |
| " | Nocturne (Petite Suite) | 48 |
| *CADMAN, CHARLES WAKEFIELD* | Mistah Shakespeah | 196 |
| *CARMICHAEL, HOAGY and JOHNNY MERCER* | Lazybones | 234 |
| *CHOPIN, FRÉDÉRIC* | Polonaise in A Major, Op. 40, No. 1 | 21 |
| *CUI, CÉSAR* | Orientale, Op. 50, No. 9 | 56 |
| *DAVIS, JIMMIE and CHARLES MITCHELL* | You are My Sunshine | 228 |
| *DEBUSSY, CLAUDE* | Prelude to the Afternoon of a Faun (Selection) | 76 |
| *DUKE, VERNON* | Brooklyn Barcarolle | 118 |
| *DYKES, JOHN B.* | Eternal Father, Strong to Save | 180 |
| *FRANCK, CÉSAR* | Panis Angelicus (Messe Solennelle) | 168 |
| *GLINKA, MICHAIL* | Russlan and Ludmilla (Selection) | 86 |
| *GOTTSCHALK, L. M.* | Berceuse | 30 |
| *GRUBER, EDMUND L.* | The Caissons Go Rolling Along (Artillery Song) | 238 |
| *HADLEY, HENRY K.* | Forever and a Day | 200 |
| *HARRIS, CHARLES K.* | After the Ball | 219 |
| *HASSLER, HANS LEO* | O Sacred Head (Salve Caput Cruentatum) | 175 |
| *HERBERT, VICTOR* | La Serenata, Op. 3 | 115 |
| *HOPKINS, EDWARD JOHN* | Saviour, Again to Thy Dear Name | 179 |
| *HOWARD, JOHN TASKER* | Still Waters | 152 |
| *HUHN, BRUNO* | Invictus | 204 |
| *KELLER, MATTHIAS* | The American Hymn | 237 |
| *KERKER, GUSTAVE* | The Belle of New York (Selection) | 102 |
| *MACDOWELL, EDWARD* | A.D. MDCXX (Sea Pieces), Op. 55, No. 3 | 59 |
| " " | From an Indian Lodge (Woodland Sketches), Op. 51, No. 5 | 62 |
| *MACGIMSEY, ROBERT* | Abraham | 194 |
| *MADRIGUERA, ENRIC* | Adios (Rhumba) | 136 |
| *MANA-ZUCCA* | Grow Old Along with Me | 212 |
| *MESSITER, ARTHUR H.* | Rejoice, Ye Pure in Heart | 178 |
| *MOZART, W. A.* | Fantasie No. 3, in D Minor | 9 |
| *MUIR, LEWIS F. and L. WOLFE GILBERT* | Waiting for the Robert E. Lee | 231 |
| *NEVIN, ETHELBERT W.* | Serenade (Good night! Good night, Beloved!) | 208 |
| *PROKOFIEFF, SERGE* | Peter and the Wolf (Selection) | 69 |
| *RAVEL, MAURICE* | Pavane | 64 |
| *RODRIGUEZ, MATOS* | La Cumparsita (Tango) | 132 |
| *ROSSINI, GIOACCHINO* | Cujus Animam (Stabat Mater) | 146 |
| *RUIZ, GABRIEL* | Amor (Bolero) | 139 |
| *SAMUELS, WALTER G.; LEONARD WHITCUP and TEDDY POWELL* | Take Me Back to My Boots and Saddle | 224 |
| *SCARLATTI, DOMENICO* | Pastorale in E Minor | 6 |
| *SCHERTZINGER, VICTOR L.* | Marcheta | 214 |
| *SCHUBERT, FRANZ* | Ave Maria | 162 |
| *SCHUMANN, ROBERT* | Romance in F sharp, Op. 28, No. 2 | 28 |
| " | The Two Grenadiers | 182 |
| *SCRIABIN, ALEXANDER* | Nocturne, Op. 9, No. 2 | 52 |
| " | Prelude, Op. 9, No. 1 | 50 |
| *SHOSTAKOVITCH, DMITRI* | Prelude in E Flat, Op. 34, No. 19 | 74 |
| *STRAUSS, RICHARD* | Allerseelen (All Souls' Day) | 188 |
| *STRAVINSKY, IGOR* | The Firebird (Selection) | 81 |
| *SWANDER, DON* | Deep in the Heart of Texas | 226 |
| *TEMPLETON, ALEC* | A Lullaby | 122 |
| " | Mozart Matriculates | 120 |
| *TSCHAIKOWSKY, P. I.* | Piano Concerto No. 1 in B Flat Minor, Op. 23 (Selection) | 41 |
| " | Romeo and Juliet (Selection) | 36 |
| *WAGNER, RICHARD* | Tristan and Isolda (Selection) | 92 |
| " | The Valkyries (Selection) | 98 |
| *WALLER, THOMAS (FATS)* | Handful of Keys | 125 |
| *WARD, SAMUEL A.* | America the Beautiful | 236 |
| *WARING, TOM* | Ol' Darkie, Ol' Mule | 191 |
| *WEBB, GEORGE J.* | Stand Up for Jesus | 178 |
| *WHITE, COOL* | Buffalo Gals | 229 |

The titles of piano compositions are printed in roman type and the titles of vocal numbers in italics.

# A Guide Through Volume IX

T HE volumes of the SCRIBNER RADIO MUSIC LIBRARY are devoted entirely to compositions which are heard constantly over the great broadcasting chains — played by orchestras, chamber music organizations, or instrumental soloists; sung by choral organizations or by vocal soloists. Each of the nine volumes contains only the choicest and most popular of its particular type of music.

---

This volume supplements the first eight volumes of the series first by supplying a number of older representative compositions which were not included in the earlier volumes, and secondly, by adding a large number of contemporary and recent pieces which have become widely used by radio stations. Among the latter are a number of copyright works by American composers which are presented with the permission of the copyright owners.

**STANDARD PIANO COMPOSITIONS**
Volume I already contains a charming piece by Domenico Scarlatti, and to this is added, in Volume IX, his lovely **Pastorale** in the famous arrangement by Carl Taussig. To the Mozart list has been added the dramatic **Fantasie No. 3 in D Minor**, long a favorite with pianists, while Beethoven's representation in the series has been increased by the melodious **Rondo in C Major.** Volume I has also a generous collection of Chopin works, but no **Polonaise**, so Volume IX offers the stirring **Military Polonaise in A Major**, which is heard frequently on the radio, not only as a piano piece but also in orchestral form. This is followed by one of the most beautiful pieces Schumann ever composed, his **Romance in F Sharp**, Op. 28, No. 2. The 19th-Century American romanticist, Louis Moreau Gottschalk, is represented by his restful **Berceuse**, which is based on an old French folk-song. Two of Tschaikowsky's most popular works are the first **Piano Concerto in B Flat Minor, Op. 23**, and the **Fantasy Overture, Romeo and Juliet.** These works are familiar on the radio, not only in their original form, but also through the numerous popular songs that have been adapted from their principal themes. They are presented here in solo piano arrangements. Next come four piano pieces by Russian composers: a quiet, restful **Nocturne** by Alexander Borodin; then two pieces by Alexander Scriabin — the **Prelude** and **Nocturne** from Op. 9, originally composed for the left-hand alone (those who find it too difficult to play the pieces in this manner may play them with both hands); and after these the famous **Orientale** by César Cui. The American Edward MacDowell is represented by two of his best-known works — **A.D.MDCXX**, from his **Sea Pieces**, Op. 55, a tone-picture of the Pilgrims' voyage in the Mayflower; and an effective number from **Woodland Sketches**, Op. 51 — **From an Indian Lodge.** These are followed by the stately and beautiful **Pavane** by the French modernist, Maurice Ravel. This piece is often heard also as an orchestral composition, and it formed the basis of a recent popular song — "The Lamp is Low." Turning again to the Russians, the modern group ends with a simplified arrangement of themes from Serge Prokofieff's Musical FairyTale for Children, **Peter and the Wolf,** and an altogether modernistic **Prelude in E Flat, Op. 34, No. 19,** by the widely-discussed Soviet composer, Dmitri Shostakovitch.

**EXCERPTS FROM BALLETS**
The older ballets are already well represented in Volume V. This Volume, therefore, presents excerpts from two modern ballets: Claude Debussy's impressionistic **Prelude to the Afternoon of a Faun;** and **Dance of the Princesses** and **Berceuse** from **The Firebird,** by the famous Russian composer, Igor Stravinsky.

**EXCERPTS FROM GRAND OPERA**
The comprehensive list in Volume IV of excerpts from Grand Operas, arranged for piano, is supplemented in this Volume by the Overture from Michail Glinka's **Russlan and Ludmilla,** in itself a most popular concert piece; and by selections from two additional Wagner operas — **The Prelude** and **Love Death** from **Tristan and Isolda;** and **Ride of the Valkyries** and **Magic Fire Music** from **The Valkyries.**

**EXCERPTS FROM LIGHT OPERA**
In this Volume a famous American operetta is added to the Light Operas of Volume V — **The Belle of New York,** by Gustave Kerker, which enjoyed popularity at the Casino Theatre, New York, in 1908, and then ran for more than two years in London. A motion picture based on this operetta has been made recently.

**LIGHT PIANO COMPOSITIONS**
All but one of the Light Compositions in Volume IX are composed by foreign-born composers who made their homes in America. Luigi Arditi, composer of the famous **Il Bacio (The Kiss)**, lived for a number of years in New York. **Il Bacio** is followed by **La Serenata, Op. 3,** by the beloved Victor Herbert. Next comes a **Brooklyn Barcarolle** by Vernon Duke, a composer of popular music who also writes serious works under his real name, Vladimir Dukelsky. The famous blind composer-pianist, Alec

Templeton, contributes his famous satire, **Mozart Matriculates** (you'll recognize its melody as that of **The Marine's Hymn**), and a charming **Lullaby** which he composed as a child. In contrast, **Handful of Keys,** by the late Thomas (Fats) Waller, famous Negro composer-pianist, is a characteristically modern piece in popular style.

**MODERN DANCE MUSIC**

The waltzes, polkas, and two-steps of Volume VI are supplemented by four modern Latin-American dance pieces: **La Cumparsita,** a Tango by Matos Rodriguez; **Adios,** a Rhumba by Enric Madriguera; **Amor,** a Bolero by Gabriel Ruiz; and **Tico-Tico,** a Samba by Zequinha Abreu. All of these are heard almost daily on the radio.

**SACRED MUSIC FOR THE PIANO**

The instrumental contents of the book close with three sacred compositions for piano: first, a solo piano arrangement of **Cujus Animam** from Rossini's **Stabat Mater;** secondly, **Still Waters** by John Tasker Howard, a Reverie on a 17th-Century tune which the Puritans sang to the 23rd Psalm; and, lastly, **At the Convent** by Alexander Borodin.

**SACRED SONGS**

The vocal section opens with a solo arrangement of a Chorale from J. S. Bach's Cantata No. 147, the lovely and justly famous **Jesu, Joy of Man's Desiring.** Next comes Schubert's **Ave Maria.** This piece is already included in Volume VII as a piano solo, but in this Volume it appears in its original form as a song, followed by the **Panis Angelicus** from César Franck's **Messe Solennelle,** and the **Agnus Dei** of Georges Bizet.

**HYMNS**

Three widely-used Catholic hymns open this section: **O Sacred Head; Jesus, My Lord, My God, My All;** and **Holy God, We Praise Thy Name.** Then comes the stirring **Rejoice, Ye Pure in Heart** and **Stand Up For Jesus,** the lovely **Saviour Again to Thy Dear Name,** and the hymn which was universally adopted by the WAVES during World War No. II, **Eternal Father Strong to Save.** The hymn section closes with the popular gospel hymn — **The Old Rugged Cross.**

**CONCERT SONGS**

Two famous songs which were not included in Volume VIII head the list of Concert Songs: Schumann's dramatic **The Two Grenadiers,** and **Allerseelen (All Soul's Day)** by Richard Strauss. Both songs are printed with English texts. Then comes a group of songs by contemporary American composers, starting with a whimsical dialect song by Tom Waring — **Ol' Darkie, Ol' Mule.** Waring is a brother of Fred Waring, whose orchestra and glee club are popular on the radio and on phonograph records. Two more dialect songs come next: **Abraham** by Robert MacGimsey, and **Mistah Shakespeah** by Charles Wakefield Cadman. The distinguished American composer, Henry K. Hadley, is represented by **Forever and a Day;** Bruno Huhn by one of America's most popular concert songs, the dramatic **Invictus;** Ethelbert Nevin by his **Serenade (Good Night! Good Night, Beloved!);** and Mana-Zucca by her setting of a Browning poem, **Grow Old Along with Me.** The section closes with two lighter concert songs, standard favorites — **Marcheta** by Victor Schertzinger and **A Little Bit of Heaven** by Ernest R. Ball.

**BALLADS AND FOLK-SONGS**

At this point Volume IX turns to popular selections which are universally featured not only on the radio but wherever there is any kind of music. First comes a song which helped to create the vogue for sentimental story-ballads — Charles K. Harris's **After the Ball,** which has become a classic. This is followed by two traditional Cowboy songs — **Home on the Range** and the Dogie song, **Whoopee Ti Yi Yo. Take Me Back to My Boots and Saddle** is a popular song in the Cowboy idiom; **Deep in the Heart of Texas** was heard on the radio dozens of times each day in the early 1940's; and **You Are My Sunshine,** which completes this classification, is a popular song in group-singing.

**PLANTATION AND MINSTREL SONGS**

The first three songs in this category are old-timers. **Buffalo Gals** is an adaptation of **Lubly Fan,** a minstrel song which was first published more than a hundred years ago. Recently its refrain "Won't you come out tonight," has been adapted to a current popular song. James A. Bland's **Carry Me Back to Old Virginny** was originally written for the minstrel shows in the late 1870's, and is now the official state song of Virginia. **Waiting for the Robert E. Lee** was first published in 1912. It was the hit-song of that year and has retained its popularity to the age of radio. The modern song in this group is Hoagy Carmichael's and Johnny Mercer's **Lazybones,** an outstanding radio favorite.

**PATRIOTIC SONGS**

Volume IX concludes with four Patriotic Songs which were not included in the patriotic material of Volume VIII: **America the Beautiful,** with words by Katharine Lee Bates; Mathias Keller's **The American Hymn;** and two famous service songs — **The Caissons Go Rolling Along** (Artillery), and **The Marine's Hymn.**

**COMPLEX INDEX**

This volume also contains a Complete Index to all of the nine volumes, cross-referenced so that all important compositions can be found under either their titles or composers; there are also a biographical, pronouncing dictionary, and a glossary of musical terms.

# Pastorale

Arranged by Carl **Tausig**.

DOMENICO SCARLATTI

# Fantasie No. 3

W. A. MOZART

# Rondo

L. VAN BEETHOVEN, Op. 51, N° 1

# Polonaise
## (Military)

FRÉDÉRIC CHOPIN, Op. 40, Nº 1.

Allegro con brio.

# Romance

ROBERT SCHUMANN Op. 28, No 2

# Berceuse
## (Cradle Song)

L. M. GOTTSCHALK

# Romeo and Juliet
## Fantasy Overture
### Selected Themes

PETER I. TSCHAIKOWSKY

Andante

# Concerto No. I, in B Flat Minor

## Selected Themes

P. I. TSCHAIKOWSKY, OP. 23

Andante non troppo

Andantino semplice

Allegro con fuoco

# Nocturne
From "Petite Suite"

ALEXANDER BORODIN

# *Prélude

ALEXANDER SCRIABIN Op. 9 Nº 1

*This Prélude, and the Nocturne which follows, were composed for the left hand alone. They may however, be played by both hands.

# *Nocturne

ALEXANDER SCRIABIN, Op.9 No.2

★ This Nocturne, and the preceding Prélude, were composed for the left hand alone. They may however, be played by both hands.

# Orientale
### From "Kaleidoscope"

CÉSAR CUI, Op. 50, No. 9

# A. D. MDCXX

From "Sea Pieces"

*The yellow setting sun*
*Melts the lazy sea to gold*
*And gilds the swaying galleon*
*That towards a land of promise*
*Lunges hugely on.*

EDWARD MACDOWELL
Op. 55, No 3.

In unbroken rolling rhythm.(♩.=58)

slightly diminish.

Sturdily and sternly, but without change of rhythm

ff

fff

$(\quad = \quad)$

fff

gradually softer

# From an Indian Lodge
From "Woodland Sketches"

EDWARD MAC DOWELL, Op. 51, No. 5

*) The low notes of the octaves carry the melody　etc.

*) The upper notes of the octaves carry the melody etc.

# Pavane

MAURICE RAVEL

Dolce e grave (♩ = 54)

Editor's note: If stretches are too wide for small hands, notes in parentheses ( ) may be omitted.

**Tempo primo**
*melodia marcata*

# Peter and the Wolf
## (A Musical Tale for Children)
### Selected Melodies

SERGE PROKOFIEFF

Moderato ♩ = 104

(Triumphal Procession)

(The Cat)

(The Procession)

L'istesso Tempo (The Duck)

(The Procession)

# Prelude

DMITRI SHOSTAKOVITCH
Op. 34, No. 19

# Prelude to the Afternoon of a Faun

Selected Themes

CLAUDE DEBUSSY

# The Firebird
## Selected Themes

Moderato (♩=72)
(Dance of the Princesses)

IGOR STRAVINSKY

Piu mosso (♩=92)

5

Piu mosso (♩ = 92)

# Russlan and Ludmilla
## Selections from the Overture

Presto M.M. ♩ = 140.

MICHAIL GLINKA

# Tristan and Isolda

### Selected Themes

RICHARD WAGNER

Lento e languido (Prelude)

Molto moderato (Isolda's Love-Death)

# The Valkyries
## Selected Themes

RICHARD WAGNER

(Ride of the Valkyries)
Allegro

(Magic Fire Scene)

101

# The Belle of New York

## Selected Melodies

GUSTAVE KERKER

Moderato (*La Belle Parisienne.*)

Moderato *(When we are married)*

Largamente (*Dance*)

Very slow Waltz tempo (*They call me the Belle of New York.*)

# Il Bacio

## (The Kiss)
### Waltz

LUIGI ARDITI

# La Serenata

VICTOR HERBERT, OPUS 3

# Brooklyn Barcarolle

VERNON DUKE

# Mozart Matriculates

ALEC TEMPLETON

# A Lullaby

ALEC TEMPLETON

Change Pedal after each change of Harmony.

# Handful of Keys

Arranged by
FRANK WELDON

THOMAS (FATS) WALLER

# La Cumparsita

Tango

MATOS RODRIGUEZ

# Adios
## Rhumba

ENRIC MADRIGUERA

Moderato assai

Smoothly

# Amor
## Bolero

GABRIEL RUIZ

Tempo di Beguine

# Tico - Tico

## Samba

ZEQUINHA ABREU

*2nd time 8va ad lib.*

# Cujus Animam
## (Stabat Mater)

GIOACCHINO ROSSINI

# Still Waters
### (Reverie on a Psalm Tune)

JOHN TASKER HOWARD

**Copyright 1945 by Quinto Maganini: Edition Musicus — New York**
**Used by Permission**

# At the Convent

From "Petite Suite"

ALEXANDER BORODIN

# Jesu, Joy of Man's Desiring

Chorale from Cantata No. 147, Arranged for
Solo Voice and Piano

J. S. BACH

With. the
Theirs is

fire    of    life _____ im - pas - sion'd.
wis - dom's    ho - liest    trea - sure.

*mp*

Striv - ing
Thou dost

*mp*

still    to    Truth    un - known,
ev - er    lead    Thine    own,

# Ave Maria

FRANZ SCHUBERT

mid _____ des-pair. Safe may we sleep un-til the

mor - row, Though ban - ish'd, out-cast and re-vil'd. Oh

Maid - en, see a maid-en's sor - row; Oh Moth - er, hear a suppliant

child! A - - ve Ma-ri - - -

a!

A - - ve Ma-

ri - - a! Stain - less

styl'd! Each fiend of — air or earthly es - sence, From

this their wont-ed haunt ex-il'd, Shall flee be-fore Thy ho-ly

pres - - ence! We bow be-neath our cares o'er

# Panis Angelicus
## (Messe Solennelle)

*English Version by*
*Sigmund Spaeth*

CÉSAR FRANCK

Pa - nis an -
O sa - cred

# Agnus Dei
### (Lamb of God)

GEORGES BIZET

A - gnus De - i!  qui  tol - lis pecca - ta mun - di,

Lamb____  of  God,  thou that  tak-est a-way the world's  guilt,

# O Sacred Head

### (Salve Caput Cruentatum)

1. O Sa - cred Head sur - round - ed By crown of pierc - ing thorn!
2. I see Thy strength and vig - or All fad - ing in the strife,
3. In this Thy bit - ter pas - sion Good Shep - herd think of me,

O bleed - ing Head, so wound - ed, Re - viled and put to scorn!
And death with cru - el rig - or Be - reav - ing Thee of life;
With Thy most sweet com - pas - sion, Un - wor - thy though I be;

Death's pal - lid hue comes o'er Thee, The glow of life de - cays,
O ag - o - ny and dy - ing! O love to sin - ners free!
Be - neath Thy Cross a - bid - ing, For - ev - er would I rest,

Yet an - gel - hosts a - dore Thee, And trem - ble as they gaze.
Je - su, all grace sup - ply - ing, O turn Thy face on me.
In Thy dear love con - fid - ing, And with Thy pres - ence blest.

# Jesus, My Lord, My God, My All

1. Je - sus, my Lord__ my God__ my All!__ How can I love Thee as I ought? And how re - vere__ this won - drous gift,__ So far sur - pass - ing hope or thought? Sweet Sac - ra - ment, We Thee__ a - dore;__ Oh! make us love Thee more__ and more; Oh! make us love Thee more__ and more.

2. Had I but Ma - ry's sin - less heart, To love Thee with, my dear - est King; Oh! with what bursts__ of fer - vent praise, Thy good-ness, Je - sus, would I sing.

3. Oh! see up - on__ the al - tar placed The Vic - tim of di - vin - est love! Let all the earth__ be - low a - dore, And join the choirs of heav'n a - bove.

4. Je - sus, dear Pas - tor of__ the flock, We crowd in love a - bout Thy feet; Our voic - es yearn__ to praise Thee, Lord, And joy - ful - ly Thy pres - ence greet.

# Holy God, We Praise Thy Name

Maestoso

1. Ho - ly God!_ we praise Thy name, Lord of all!_ we bow_ be - fore Thee; All on earth Thy scep - tre claim, All in heav'n a - bove_ a - dore Thee; In - fi - nite_ Thy vast do - main, Ev - er - last - ing is_ Thy reign.

2. Hark! the loud_ ce - les - tial hymn, An - gel choirs a - bove_ are rais - ing; Cher - u - bim_ and Ser - a - phim In un - ceas - ing chor - us prais - ing; Fill the heav'ns with sweet ac - cord: Ho - ly, Ho - ly, Ho - ly Lord!

3. Ho - ly Fa - ther, Ho - ly Son, Ho - ly Spir - it, Three we name Thee, While in es - sence on - ly One, Un - di - vid - ed God we claim Thee: And a - dor - ing bend the knee, While we own_ the mys - ter - y.

# Rejoice, Ye Pure in Heart

EDWARD H. PLUMPTRE

ARTHUR M. MESSITER

1. Re - joice, ye__ pure in heart, Re - joice, give thanks and sing:
2. With all the__ an - gel choirs, With all the saints on earth,
3. Still lift your__ stand - ard high, Still march in firm ar - ray;
4. Yes, on through life's long path, Still chant - ing as ye go;
5. Then on, ye__ pure in heart, Re - joice, give thanks, and sing;

Your fes - tal ban - ner wave on high, The cross of Christ your King.
Pour out the strains of joy and bliss, True rap - ture, no - blest mirth!
As war - riors through the dark - ness toil Till dawns the gold - en day.
From youth to age, by night and day, In glad - ness and in woe.
Your fes - tal ban - ner wave on high, The cross of Christ your King.

REFRAIN

Re - joice, re - joice, Re - joice, give thanks, and sing! A - men.

Re - joice, re - joice,

# Stand Up for Jesus

GEORGE DUFFIELD

GEORGE J. WEBB

1. Stand up, stand up for Je - sus, Ye sol - diers of the cross, Lift high His roy - al
2. Stand up, stand up for Je - sus, The trump - et call o - bey; Forth to the might - y
3. Stand up, stand up for Je - sus, Stand in His strength a - lone; The arm of flesh will
4. Stand up, stand up for Je - sus, The strife will not be long; This day the noise of

ban-ner, It must not suf-fer loss; From vic-tory un-to vic-tory, His
con-flict, In this His glor-ious day. "Ye, that are men, now serve Him", A-
fail you Ye dare not trust your own; Put on the gos-pel ar-mor, Each
bat-tle, The next, the vic-tor's song; To him that o-ver-com-eth, A

ar-my shall He lead, Till ev-ery foe is van-quished And Christ is Lord in-deed.
gainst un-num-bered foes; Let cour-age rise with dan-ger, And strength to strength op-pose.
piece put on with prayer; Where du-ty calls, or dan-ger, Be nev-er want-ing there.
crown of life shall be; He with the King of glo-ry Shall reign e-ter-nal-ly. A-men.

## Saviour Again to Thy Dear Name

JOHN ELLERTON

EDWARD J. HOPKINS

1. Sav-iour, a-gain to Thy dear name we raise With one ac-cord our
2. Grant us Thy peace up-on our home-ward way; With Thee be-gan, with
3. Grant us Thy peace, Lord, thro' the com-ing night, Turn Thou for us its
4. Grant us Thy peace through-out our earth-ly life, Our balm in sor-row,

part-ing hymn of praise; We stand to bless Thee ere our wor-ship
Thee shall end the day; Guard Thou the lips from sin, the hearts from
dark-ness in-to light; From harm and dan-ger keep Thy chil-dren
and our stay in strife; Then, when Thy voice shall bid our con-flict

cease, Then, low-ly kneel-ing, wait Thy word of peace.
shame, That in this house have called up-on Thy name.
free, For dark and light are both a-like to Thee.
cease, Call us, O Lord, to Thine e-ter-nal peace.

# Eternal Father, Strong to Save

WILLIAM WHITING

JOHN B. DYKES

**With dignity**

1. E - ter - nal Fa - ther, strong to save, Whose arm doth bind the
2. O Sav - iour, whose al - might - y word The winds and waves sub -
3. O sa - cred Spir - it, who didst brood Up - on the cha - os
4. O Trin - i - ty of love and power, Our breth - ren shield in

rest - less wave, Who bidd'st the might - y o - cean deep
mis - sive heard, Who walk - edst on the foam - ing deep
dark and rude, Who bad'st its an - gry tu - mult cease,
dan - ger's hour; From rock and tem - pest, fire and foe,

Its own ap - point - ed lim - its keep: O hear us when we
And calm a - mid its rage didst sleep: O hear us when we
And gav - est light and life and peace: O hear us when we
Pro - tect them wher - so - e'er they go; And ev - er let there

cry to Thee For those in per - il on the sea.
cry to Thee For those in per - il on the sea.
cry to Thee For those in per - il on the sea.
rise to Thee Glad hymns of praise from land and sea. A - men.

# The Old Rugged Cross

Rev. GEO. BENNARD

1. On a hill far a-way stood an old rug-ged cross, The em-blem of suf-f'ring and shame; And I love that old cross where the dear-est and best For a world of lost sin-ners was slain.
2. Oh, that old rug-ged cross, so de-spised by the world, Has a won-drous at-trac-tion for me; For the dear Lamb of God left His glo-ry a-bove To bear it to dark Cal-va-ry.
3. In the old rug-ged cross, stained with blood so di-vine, A won-drous beau-ty I see; For 'twas on that old cross Je-sus suf-fered and died To par-don and sanc-ti-fy me.
4. To the old rug-ged cross I will ev-er be true, Its shame and re-proach glad-ly bear; Then He'll call me some day to my home far a-way, Where His glo-ry for-ev-er I'll share.

CHORUS

So I'll cher-ish the old rug-ged cross, Till my tro-phies at last I lay down; I will cling to the old rug-ged cross, And ex-change it some day for a crown.

cross, the old rug-ged cross, cross, the old rug-ged cross,

# The Two Grenadiers

HEINRICH HEINE

ROBERT SCHUMANN

Franc - e's proud realm had been shak - en, De - feat - ed and scat - ter'd the

val - i-ant host, And the emp-'ror, the emp-'ror'd been tak-en.

How bit - ter-ly wept then the gren-a - diers, At hear-ing the ter - ri-ble

sto - ry; And one then said: "A-las! once more My wounds are bleed-ing and

Then on my bos - om place thou, Give me my mus-ket in my

hand, My sword a - round me brace thou. Thus

will I lis - ten and lie so still, And watch like a guard o'er the

forc - es, Un - til the roar - ing of can - non I hear, And

tramp-ing of neigh-ing hors-es. Then o-ver my grave will my Em-per-or ride, While

swords gleam bright-ly and rat-tle, While swords gleam bright-ly and

rat-tle; Then arm'd to the teeth will I rise from the grave, For my

Emp'ror, my Emp'ror to bat-tle.

# Allerseelen
## (All Soul's Day)

HERMANN VON GILM
English version by
Sigmund Spaeth

RICHARD STRAUSS
Op. 10, No. 8

Bring back to life  a fra-grant mem-'ry's

tok - en, The last red flow'rs of grief be-side me  lay,  And let our words of love a-gain  be

bloom, __ no more the grave __ can hold you, Once in the year we give the

dead their day, Come to my heart, _____ and let my love en-fold you, As once in

May, As once in

May.

# Ol' Darkie, Ol' Mule

JACK DOLPH                                                           TOM WARING

Ol' grey dark - ie, ol'_____ grey mule,_

Ol' grey dark-ie, ol'_____ grey mule, Go - in'

# Abraham

ROBERT MAC GIMSEY

I'm goin' to rest on the bo-som of Ab-ra-ham, Ab-ra-ham, Ab - ra-ham, I'm goin' to
I'm goin' to eat at the ta-ble with Ab-ra-ham, Ab-ra-ham, Ab - ra-ham, And I'll have
I'm goin' to walk a-round hea-ven with Ab-ra-ham, Ab-ra-ham, Ab - ra-ham, Walk down the

rest on the bo-som of Ab - ra-ham, When the an-gels car-ry me home, I'm goin' to
chick - en, am-bro-si - a and ho-ney lamb, When the an-gels car-ry me home, I'm goin' to
streets that are paved — with gold, ____ When the an-gels car-ry me home, I'm goin' to

REFRAIN

# Mistah Shakespeah

HAZEL DELL CRANDALL

CHARLES WAKEFIELD CADMAN

**Lively, and with jollity**

Mis - tah Shakespeah sho' wuz know-in', wuz know-in', Dat's how he done cotched his

fame ___ Mis - tah Shake-speah sho' wuz know-in' when he

sayed, "What's in a name?" ___

# Forever and a Day

THOMAS BAILEY ALDRICH

HENRY K. HADLEY, Op. 12, No. 1

I lit-tle know or care If the black-bird on the bough Is fill-ing all the air With his soft cre-scen-dos

day. _____ It's lit-tle that I

mind How the blos-soms pink or white, At eve-ry touch of

wind Fall a-trem-bling with de-light; For in the leaf-y

lane, Be-neath the gar-den boughs, And through the si-lent

# Invictus

WILLIAM ERNEST HENLEY

BRUNO HUHN

Out of the night that cov-ers me, Black as the pit from pole to pole, I

thank what-ev-er gods may be For my__ un-con-quer-a-ble soul.

# Serenade
### (Good-night! good-night, beloved!)

ETHELBERT NEVIN

# Grow Old Along with Me

ROBERT BROWNING

MANA-ZUCCA, Op. 152

Grow__ old a - long with me The best is yet to be, The last of life,__ For which the first was made:__ Our times are in His hand Who saith, "A whole I

# Marcheta
## (A Love Song of Old Mexico)

Words and Music by
VICTOR L. SCHERTZINGER

# A Little Bit of Heaven

J. KEIRN BRENNAN

ERNEST R. BALL

here's the way me dear old moth-er told the tale to me.___
lit - tle bit of Heav - en, and I love it more and more.___

Shure, a lit - tle bit of Heav - en fell from out the sky one day,___ and

nes - tled on the o - cean in a spot so far a - way;___ And

when the An - gels found it, shure it looked so sweet and fair,___ they

# After the Ball

CHAS. K. HARRIS

Have you no ba - bies, have you no home?_____
I wish some wa - ter; leave me a - lone!_____
I would not list - en, plead - ings were vain,_____

I had a sweet - heart, years, years a - go;_____
When I re - turned dear, there stood a man,_____
One day a let - ter came, from that man,_____

Where she is now pet, you will soon know._____
Kiss - ing my sweet - heart as lov - ers can._____
He was her broth - er the let - ter ran._____

List to the stor - y, I'll tell it all,_____
Down fell the glass, pet, brok - en, that's all,_____
That's why I'm lone - ly, no home at all,_____

I be - lieved her faith - less, af - ter the ball.
Just as my heart was, af - ter the ball.
I broke her heart pet, af - ter the ball.

CHORUS

Af-ter the ball is o - ver, Af-ter the break of morn, ___
Af-ter the danc-ers leav - ing, Af-ter the stars are
gone; ___ Man-y a heart is ach - ing, if you could
read them all; ___ Man-y the hopes that have van - ished,

1. Af - ter the ball. ___ 2. ball.

# Home on the Range

Cowboy Song

**Allegro moderato**

1. Oh give me a home where the buf-fa-lo roam Where the
2. Where the air is so pure, and the zeph-yrs so free And the
3. How oft-en at night, when the heav-ens are bright With the

deer and the an-te-lope play, Where sel-dom is heard a dis-
breez-es so balm-y and light, That I would not ex-change my
light from the glit-ter-ing stars, Have I stood there a-mazed and

cour-ag-ing word, And the skies are not cloud-y all day.
home on the range, For all of the cit-ies so bright.
asked as I gazed If their glo-ry ex-ceeds that of ours.

CHORUS

Home, home on the range Where the deer and the an-te-lope play. Where

sel-dom is heard a dis-cour-ag-ing word And the skies are not cloud-y all day.

# Whoopee Ti Yi Yo

Cowboy Song

# Take Me Back to My
# Boots and Saddle

WALTER G. SAMUELS
LEONARD WHITCUP
and TEDDY POWELL

Copyright 1935 by La Salle Music Publishers, Inc.
Used by Permission

# Deep in the Heart of Texas

JUNE HERSHEY

DON SWANDER

Clap

Deep in the heart of Tex-as; The prair-ie
Deep in the heart of Tex-as; The rab-bits

Clap Clap Clap Clap

sky is wide and high, Deep in the heart of
rush a-round the brush, Deep in the heart of

Tex-as. The sage in bloom is like per-
Tex-as. The cow-boys cry, "Ki-yip-pee-

Clap Clap Clap Clap

fume, Deep in the heart of Tex-as, Re-
yi," Deep in the heart of Tex-as, The

Clap Clap Clap Clap

minds me of the one I love, Deep in the
dog-ies bawl, and bawl and bawl, Deep in the

1.
heart of Tex-as. The
2.
heart of Tex-as.

8

# You Are My Sunshine

JIMMIE DAVIS and
CHARLES MITCHELL

# Buffalo Gals

COOL WHITE

**Allegro**

1. As I was walk-ing down the street, Down the street, down the street, A
2. I stopped her and we had some talk, Had some talk, had some talk, But her
3. Her lips are like the oys-ter plant, Oys-ter plant, oys-ter plant, I
4. I asked this girl to be my wife, Be my wife, be my wife, Then

pret-ty gal I chanc'd to meet, O she was fair to view.
foot cov-er'd up the whole side walk And left no room for me.
try to kiss 'em but I can't They are so ver-y large.
I'd be hap-py all my life And skip to the love-ly moon.

**CHORUS**

Buf-fa-lo gals, Will you come out to-night, Will you come out to-night, Will you come out to-night?

Buf-fa-lo gals, Will you come out to-night, And dance by the light of the moon.

# Carry Me Back to Old Virginny

JAMES A. BLAND

# Waiting for the Robert E. Lee

L. WOLFE GILBERT

LEWIS F. MUIR

CHORUS

Watch them shuff - lin' a - long;

See them shuff - lin' a - long _____ Go take your

# Lazybones

JOHNNY MERCER and
HOAGY CARMICHAEL

**Slow Blues**

Long as there is chick-en gra-vy on your rice, ev'ry-thing is nice.

Long as there's a wa-ter-mel-on on the vine, Ev'ry-thing is fine. You got no time to work, you got no time to play,

Bus-y do-in' noth-in' all the live-long day. You won't ev-er change no mat-ter what I say You're just made that way.

**CHORUS**

La - zy-bones, Sleep in' in the sun, How you 'spec' to get your day's work done? Nev-er get your day's work done,        Sleep-in' in the noon-day sun.        La - zy-bones, sleep-in' in the shade,

How you 'spec' to get your corn meal made?   Nev-er get your corn meal made.        Sleep-in' in the eve-nin'

shade.      When 'ta - ters   need spray-in',   I   bet you   keep pray-in'   the bugs fall off of the

vine ———— And when you go fish - in' I   bet you keep wish-in' The fish won't grab at your   line.

La - zy-bones, loaf-in' thru the day,   How you 'spec' to make a dime that way? Nev-er make a dime that

*(Spoken or sung)*

way (well look-y here,)     He nev - er heared a word I   say!        say !

**1**      **2**

*mf*   *rit*

R.H.

Ped.

# America the Beautiful

KATHERINE LEE BATES

SAMUEL A. WARD

1. O beau-ti-ful for spa-cious skies, For am-ber waves of grain,___ For
2. O beau-ti-ful for pil-grim feet, Whose stern, im-pas-sioned stress,___ A
3. O beau-ti-ful for he-roes proved In lib-er-at-ing strife,___ Who
4. O beau-ti-ful for pa-triot dream That sees be-yond the years___ Thine

pur - ple moun-tain maj - es-ties A - bove the fruit-ed plain!___ A -
thor - ough-fare for free-dom beat A - cross the wil-der-ness!___ A -
more than self their coun-try loved, And mer - cy more than life!___ A -
al - a - bas-ter cit - ies gleam, Un - dimmed by hu-man tears!___ A -

mer - i - ca! A - mer - i - ca! God shed His grace on thee,___ And
mer - i - ca! A - mer - i - ca! God mend thine ev - 'ry flaw,___ Con-
mer - i - ca! A - mer - i - ca! May God thy gold re - fine,___ Till
mer - i - ca! A - mer - i - ca! God shed His grace on thee,___ And

crown thy good with broth - er - hood From sea to shin - ing sea!
firm thy soul in self - con - trol, Thy lib - er - ty in law!
all suc - cess be no - ble-ness, And ev - 'ry grace di - vine!
crown thy good with broth - er - hood From sea to shin - ing sea!

# The American Hymn

(Speed Our Republic)

MATTHIAS KELLER

Maestoso

1. Speed our re - pub - lic, O Fa - ther on high! Lead us in path-ways of
2. Faith-ful and hon-est to friend and to foe Will-ing to die_ in hu-
3. Rise up, proud ea - gle, rise up to the clouds, Spread thy broad wings o'er this

jus-tice and right; Rul - ers as well as the ruled, "One and all," Gir - dle with
man - i - ty's cause— Thus we de - fy all ty - ran - ni - cal pow'r, While we con -
fair west-ern world! Fling from thy beak our dear ban - ner of old— Show that it

vir - tue the ar - mor of might! Hail! three times hail_ to our coun-try and flag!
tend for our Un - ion and laws! Hail! three times hail_ to our coun-try and flag!
still is for free-dom un-furl'd! Hail! three times hail_ to our coun-try and flag!

CHORUS

Rul - ers as well as the ruled, "One and all," Gir - dle with vir - tue the
Thus we de - fy_ all ty - ran - ni - cal pow'r, While we con - tend for our
Fling from thy beak our dear ban - ner of old, Show that it still is for

ar - mor of might! Hail! three times hail_ to our coun-try and flag!
Un - ion and laws! Hail! three times hail_ to our coun-try and flag!
free-dom un-furl'd! Hail! three times hail_ to our coun-try and flag!

# The Caissons Go Rolling Along

(Artillery Song)

EDMUND L. GRUBER

March time

O-ver hill, o-ver dale, We have hit the dust-y trail, And those
To the front, day and night, Where the dough-boys dig and fight And those

cais-sons go roll-ing a - long———— "Coun-ter march! Right a - bout!" Hear those
cais-sons go roll-ing a - long———— Our bar - rage will be there Fi - red

wa-gon sol-diers shout, While those cais-sons go roll-ing a - long:———
on the rock-et's flare While those cais-sons go roll-ing a - long:———

# The Marine's Hymn

Arranged by Luis Guzmán
U. S. Marine Band

March tempo

1. From the Halls of Mon - te - zu - ma To the shores of Trip - o -
2. Our flag's un - furl'd to ev - 'ry breeze From dawn to set - ting
3. Here's health to you and to our Corps Which we are proud to

li; We fight our coun-try's bat - tles In the air, on land and
sun; We have fought in ev - 'ry clime and place Where we could take a
serve; In many a strife we've fought for life And nev - er lost our

sea; First to fight for right and free - dom And to keep our hon-or clean;
gun; In the snow of far off North-ern lands And in sun - ny trop-ic scenes;
nerve; If the Ar - my and the Na - vy Ev - er look on Heav-en's scenes;

We are proud to claim the ti - tle Of U-nit-ed States Ma-rines.
You will find us al - ways on the job The U-nit-ed States Ma-rines.
They will find the streets are guard - ed By U-nit-ed States Ma-rines.

As published by "The Leatherneck"
with special Permission
of the
United States Marine Corps.

# BRIEF BIOGRAPHICAL AND PRONOUNCING DICTIONARY OF COMPOSERS

*Originally compiled by Albert E. Wier. Composers in Volume Nine added by John Tasker Howard*

The following list contains the names of the principal composers, whose works are to be found in "The Scribner Radio Music Library." Concise biographical information for ready reference has been given in most instances, also the pronunciation of foreign names on a simple phonetic system. Wherever possible, a systematic method of giving information has been adhered to, consisting of the surname, Christian name, pronunciation, nationality, field of effort, dates of birth and death (unless contemporaneous), and the name of best-known individual composition.

**Abt, Franz** (Ahbt). German song-writer, 1819–85. "When the Swallows Homeward Fly."

**Adam, Adolph** (Ah'dam). French comic-opera composer, 1803–56. "Si j'etais Roi."

**Adams, Stephen.** See Maybrick, M.

**Albeniz, Isaac.** (All-bay'niz). Spanish composer and pianist, 1860-1909. Many charming salon compositions.

**Ambrose, R. S.** American composer of sacred songs. "One Sweetly Solemn Thought."

**Arditi, Luigi** (Ahr-dee'tee). Italian composer and opera conductor, 1822–1903. "Il Bacio."

**Ascher, Joseph.** Dutch pianist-composer, 1829-69. "Alice Where Art Thou?"

**Auber, Daniel** (Oh'behr). French light-opera composer, 1782-1871. "Fra Diavolo."

**Audran, Edward** (Oh-drahn'). French light-opera composer, 1842–1901. "The Mascot" and "Olivette."

**Bach, Johann Sebastian** (Bahkh). German classical composer, 1685–1750. Church music, organ music, orchestral and chamber music, clavier pieces.

**Bachmann, Georges** (Bahkh'-mann). French composer, 1848-94. "Les Sylphes."

**Balfe, Michael.** Irish operatic composer, 1808–70. "Bohemian Girl" and "Killarney."

**Ball, Ernest R.** American song-composer, 1878-1927. "A Little Bit of Heaven," "Mother Machree," etc.

**Barnard, Mrs. Charles.** See Claribel.

**Barnby, Sir Joseph.** English organist-composer, 1838-96. "Sweet and Low."

**Beethoven, Ludwig van** (Bay'toh-ven). One of the greatest German composers, 1770–1827. Symphonies, chamber music, and piano works.

**Bellini, Vincenzo** (Bell-een'ee). Italian operatic composer, 1801–35. "Norma," "La Sonnambula."

**Bishop, Sir Henry.** English composer, 1786-1855. "Home, Sweet Home."

**Bizet, Georges** (Bee'zay). French operatic composer, 1838–75. "Carmen."

**Bland, James A.** Negro composer and minstrel performer, 1845-1911. "Carry Me Back to Old Virginny," "Oh! dem Golden Slippers," etc.

**Blon, Franz von.** German bandmaster and composer of salon music, 1861– —. "Sizilietta."

**Boccherini, Luigi** (Boch-er-ee'nee). Italian cellist-composer, 1743-1805. "Minuet in A."

**Bohm, Karl** (Bowm). German pianist-composer, 1844-1920. "Still as the Night."

**Boito, Arrigo** (Bo'e-toh). Italian opera composer and librettist. 1842-1918.

**Borodin, Alexander** (Bor-oh-deen'). Russian composer, 1833–1887. Opera "Prince Igor," "Petite Suite" for piano.

**Borowski, Felix.** English-born American composer, 1872– —. "La Coquette," "Valsette."

**Bosc, August** (Bosk). French composer of light music. "Rose Mousse."

**Bourgeois, Loys** (Boor-zhwah'). 16th century French sacred-music composer, follower of Calvin. Writer of well-known hymn tunes.

**Bradbury, W. B.** American composer. 1816-68. "Sweet Hour of Prayer."

**Braga, Gaetano** (Brah'gah). Italian cellist-composer, 1829-1907. "Angel's Serenade."

**Brahms, Johannes.** One of the greatest German composers, 1833–97. Symphonies, chamber music, piano works, songs.

**Bucalossi, Ernest** (Boo-ka-loss'si). English dance-music composer. "La Gitana" Waltzes.

**Cadman, Charles Wakefield.** American composer, 1881– —. Operas, orchestral music, piano pieces, songs.

**Carey, Henry.** English song-writer, 1685–1743. *Said* to have written "God Save the King," *known* to have written "Sally in Our Alley."

**Carmichael, Hoagy.** American composer of popular music, 1903– —. "Lazybones," "Star Dust," etc.

**Chabrier, Emmanuel** (Shah'br'ya'). French composer, 1841–94. "España," a Spanish rhapsody.

**Chaminade, Cécile** (Sha'mee-nahd). French composer and pianist, 1857–1944. Light piano pieces.

**Chevalier, Auguste** (She-val'ya). Brother of Albert Chevalier, the famous English coster singer, for whose songs (such as "My Old Dutch") he has composed the music under the name of "Charles Ingle."

**Chopin, Frédéric.** Polish composer, 1810–49. Romantic piano compositions.

**Claribel** (**Mrs. Charles Barnard**). English popular-song writer, 1830-69. "I Cannot Sing the Old Songs," "Come Back to Erin."

**Clay, Frederic.** English composer, born in Paris, 1838-89. Ballad operas and songs such as "I'll Sing Thee Songs of Araby."

**Converse, Charles.** American composer, 1832-1918. "What a Friend We Have in Jesus."

**Cui, César.** Russian composer, 1835-1918. Instrumental pieces: "Orientale," etc.

**Czibulka, Alphonse** (Tche-bool'ka). Hungarian bandmaster-composer, 1842-94. "Stephanie" Gavotte.

**Debussy, Claude** (Dŭ-bü'say). French impressionist composer, 1862-1918. Piano music, songs, orchestral works, opera "Pelleas et Melisande," ballet "Prelude to the Afternoon of a Faun."

**Delibes, Clément** (Deh-leeb'). French dramatic composer, 1836-91. "Sylvia" Ballet.

**Denza, Luigi** (Den'tsa). Italian song composer, 1846-1922. "Funiculi, Funicula."

**Dittersdorf, Karl von.** Austrian symphonic composer, 1739-99. "German Dance."

**Donizetti, Gaetano** (Don-i-tset-ti). Italian operatic composer, 1797-1848. "Lucia di Lammermoor."

**Drdla, Franz** (Derd'-la). Austrian composer and violinist, 1868– —. His "Souvenir" and other salon pieces are very popular.

**Drigo, Richard.** Italian ballet director and composer, 1846-1930. "Les Millions d'Arlequin."

**Duke, Vernon.** Russian-born American composer of popular music, (real name Vladimir Dukelsky, under which he composes orchestral and concert music), 1903– —. "Brooklyn Barcarolle."

**Durand, Auguste** (Du'ron). French composer and music publisher for Massenet, Saint-Saëns, and many others, 1830-1909.

**Dvořák, Antonin** (Dvor'zhahk). Bohemian composer, 1841-1904. "New World Symphony" and a "Humoresque."

**Dykes, Rev. J. B.** English church-music composer, 1823-76. "Lead, Kindly Light," "Eternal Father, Strong to Save."

**Eilenberg, Richard.** Well-known German composer of dance music. "First Heart Throbs" Gavotte.

**Elgar, Sir Edward.** English composer, 1857-1934. "Pomp and Circumstance, "Salut 'Aamour," etc.

**Falla, Manuel de** (Fah'yah). Spanish composer, 1876– —. Grand operas, "La Vida Breve."

**Fauré, Gabriel** (Foh-ray'). French composer, 1845-1924. "Romance Sans Paroles."

**Faure, J. Baptiste** (Fohr). French composer, 1830-1914. "Palm Branches."

**Fibich, Zdenko.** Bohemian composer, 1850-1900. "Poëme," popularized as a violin solo by Kubelik.

**Field, John.** Irish pianist-composer, 1782-1837. Nocturnes.

**Flotow, Friedrich** (Floh'toh). German operatic composer, 1812-83. "Martha."

**Fontenailles, H. de** (Fon-te-nah'yee). French composer of sentimental songs. "Obstination."

**Foster, Stephen.** American composer, 1826-64. Songs of the South such as "My Old Kentucky Home," "Old Folks at Home."

**Franck, César** (Frahnck). Belgian composer, 1822-1890. Church music, chamber music, "Symphony in D Minor," "Messe Solennelle."

**Franke, Th.** (Frank'eh). French composer of light pieces. "Intermezzo Russe."

**Gabriel, Virginia.** English song composer, 1825–77. "Only a Face at the Window."

**Gade, Niels W.** (Gah'de). Danish composer, 1817–90. Symphonies, Part Songs and Cantatas.

**Ganne, Louis** (Gahn). French composer, 1862–1923. Light opera and salon music such as "L'Extase."

**Gaul, Alfred.** English conductor-composer, 1837–1913. Cantata, "The Holy City."

**Gautier, Louis** (Goht'yea). French composer of light piano music. "Le Secret."

**German, Edward.** English composer, 1862–1936. Light operas and incidental music such as "Henry VIII" Dances.

**Gillet, Ernest** (Ghil'lay). French cellist-composer, 1856– —. "Loin du Bal."

**Glazounov, Alexander** (Glah-zoo-nohv'). Russian composer, 1865–1936. Symphonies and operatic compositions.

**Glinka, Michail.** Russian nationalist composer, 1804–1857. Operas, "A Life for the Czar," "Russlan and Ludmilla."

**Gluck, C. W. von** (Glook). German operatic composer, 1714–87. "Iphigénie en Aulide," "Orphée."

**Godard, Benjamin** (Goh-dahr). French composer, 1849–95. "Second Mazurka."

**Goldmark, Karl.** Hungarian operatic composer, 1830–1915. "Queen of Sheba."

**Goodeve, Arthur.** American composer of songs such as "Fiddle and I."

**Gossec, Joseph.** Dutch composer, 1734–1829. Operas and string quartets.

**Gottschalk, Louis Moreau.** American composer-pianist, 1829–1869. Piano pieces, "The Last Hope," "The Banjo," "Berceuse," etc.

**Gounod, Charles** (Goo'no). French operatic and sacred-music composer. 1818–93. "Faust" and "Ave Maria."

**Granados, Enrique** (Grah-nah'-dos). Spanish composer, 1867–1916, of piano music and operas. Drowned on the English steamship *Sussex*, which was torpedoed during World War I.

**Gray, Hamilton.** American composer of sacred songs such as "A Dream of Paradise."

**Grieg, Edvard** (Greeg). Norwegian pianist and composer, 1843–1907. Songs, pianoforte pieces, symphonies, etc.

**Gung'l, Joseph** (Goong'ul). Hungarian bandmaster-composer, 1810–89. "Oberlandler" Waltzes.

**Hadley, Henry K.** American composer, 1871–1937. Symphonies, operas, piano music, songs.

**Handel, G. F.** (Han'del). German operatic and oratorio composer, 1685–1759. "Largo."

**Harris, Charles K.** American composer of popular ballads, 1865–1930. "After the Ball."

**Harrison, Annie Fortescue.** English composer of semi-popular songs, 1849–1944. "In the Gloaming."

**Hassler, Hans Leo.** German organist and composer, 1564–1612. Church music. "O Sacred Head."

**Hastings, Thomas.** American composer and writer, 1784–1872. "Rock of Ages."

**Hauser, Miska.** Hungarian violinist-composer, 1822–87. "Cradle Song."

**Haydn, Josef** (Hide'n). German composer, 1732–1809. Oratorios, symphonies, and string quartets.

**Heller, Stephen.** Hungarian pianist-composer, 1813–88. "Tarantelle."

**Herbert, Victor.** Irish-born American composer, 1859–1924. Operettas, orchestral music, piano pieces.

**Hérold, Louis** (Ay-roh'd). French operatic composer, 1791–1833. "Zampa."

**Hollaender, Victor.** German comic-opera composer, 1866– —. "Sumurun."

**Hopkins, Edward John.** English composer of Church music, 1818–1901. "Saviour Again to Thy Dear Name."

**Howard, John Tasker.** American composer and author, 1890– —. "Still Waters."

**Huhn, Bruno.** English-born American composer of songs. 1871– —. "Invictus."

**Humperdinck, Engelbert.** German operatic composer, 1854–1921. "Hansel and Gretel."

**Iljinsky, Alexander** (Il-yin'sky). Russian composer, 1859–1919. "Cradle Song."

**Ippolitov-Iwanov, Michael.** Russian composer, 1859–1935. "Caucasian Sketches."

**Ivanovici, J.** (E-van-o-vee'kee). Roumanian bandmaster and composer of dance music, died 1902.

**Jakobowski, Edward** (Yak-o-boff-sky). Well-known comic-opera composer, 1858– —. "Erminie."

**Jensen, Adolf** (Yen'sen). German composer, 1837–79. "Murmuring Zephyrs."

**Keller, Matthias.** German-born American violinist and composer, 1813–1875. "The American Hymn."

**Kerker, Gustav.** German-born American composer of operettas, 1857–1923. "The Belle of New York."

**Key, Francis Scott.** Poet, 1780–1843. Author of "Star-Spangled Banner."

**Kingsley, Charles.** Noted English divine, novelist, and poet. Author of "Three Fishers."

**Kistler, Cyrill.** German opera composer, 1848–1907. "Kunihild."

**Kittredge, Walter.** American poet and composer. Born 1832. "Tenting To-night."

**Kjerulf, Halfdan** (Yha'-rulf). Norwegian composer, 1815–68. "Last Night."

**Knecht, J. H.** (Nekt). German organist-composer, 1752–1817. "O Jesus Thou Art Standing."

**Knight, J. P.** English composer, 1812–87. "Rocked in the Cradle of the Deep."

**Koschat, Thomas.** German composer, 1845–1914. "Forsaken."

**Lack, Théodore** (Lahk). French composer, 1846–1921. Light piano pieces.

**Lacome, Paul Jean Jacques.** French light-opera composer, 1838–1920. Suite "La Feria."

**Lassen, Eduard** (Lah'sen). Danish composer, 1830–1904. "Thine Eyes So Blue and Tender."

**Lasson, Per.** Swedish composer of very popular piano pieces and songs.

**Lavallée, Calixa** (Lah-vahl-lay'). Canadian pianist-composer, 1842–91. "The Butterfly."

**Lecocq, Charles** (Lu-kohk). French light-opera composer, 1832–1918. "Giroflé-Giroflá."

**Lehar, Franz.** Viennese comic-opera composer, 1870– —. "Merry Widow."

**Lemare, Edwin H.** English organist-composer, 1865–1934. "Andantino."

**Leoncavallo, Ruggiero.** Italian composer, 1858–1919. Operatic composer, "Pagliacci," "Zaza."

**Levine, M.** Russian composer of light piano music.

**Liadov, Anatol** (L'yah'-doff). Russian composer, 1855–1914. "A Musical Snuff-Box."

**Liszt, Franz** (List). Hungarian piano virtuoso and composer, 1811–86. "Hungarian Rhapsodies."

**Lover, Samuel.** Irish novelist, poet, and composer, 1797–1868. "Low-Backed Car."

**Lowry, Robert.** American hymn composer, 1826–1899. "Shall We Gather at the River?"

**Luigini, Alexandre.** French light-opera and ballet composer, 1850–1906. "Egyptian Ballet."

**Macbeth, Allan.** Scotch composer, 1856–1910. "Forget-Me-Not" Intermezzo.

**MacDowell, Edward.** American pianist-composer, 1861–1908. "Hexantanz," "Woodland Sketches," "Sea Pieces."

**MacGimsey, Robert.** American composer of Negro dialect songs, 1898– —. "Abraham."

**Mana-Zucca.** American composer, 1890– —. Piano pieces, songs. "Grow Old Along with Me."

**Margis, A.** French composer, 1874– —. "Valse Bleue."

**Marie, Gabriel** (Mar-ee'). French composer, 1852–1928. "La Cinquantaine."

**Martini, Giambattista** (Mahr-tee'-nee). Italian priest and composer, 1706–1784. "Gavotte."

**Mascagni, Pietro** (Mahs-kahn'yee). Italian opera composer, 1863–1945. "Cavalleria Rusticana."

**Mason, Lowell.** American hymn composer and music compiler, 1792–1872. "From Greenland's Icy Mountains."

**Massenet, Jules** (Mahss-nay'). French composer, 1842–1912. "Thais."

**Mattei, Tito** (Mat-tay'ee). Italian song composer, 1841–1914. "Non é Ver."

**Maybrick, M.** (Stephen Adams). English singer and popular-song composer, 1844–1913. "Mona."

**Mendelssohn, Bartholdy, Felix** (Men-del-soan-Bar-tole'dy). German composer, 1809–47. Symphonies, choral works, piano music, songs.

**Messiter, Arthur Henry.** English-born American organist and choirmaster, 1834–1916. "Rejoice Ye Pure in Heart."

**Meyerbeer, Giacomo** (My'er-baer). German operatic composer, 1791–1864. "Les Huguenots."

**Meyer-Helmund, Erik.** Russian composer, 1861–1932. Operas and piano music.

**Millocker, Karl.** Viennese light-opera composer, 1842–1899. "Beggar Student."

**Molloy, J. L.** Irish composer, 1837–1909. "Love's Old Sweet Song."

**Monk, W. H.** English organist-composer, 1823–89. "Abide with Me."

**Moore, Thomas.** Irish poet and composer, 1779–1852. "Believe Me If All Those Endearing Young Charms."

**Moszkowski, Moritz** (Mohsh-koff'sky). German (born Polish) pianist-composer, 1854–1925. "Serenade" and "Spanish Dances."

**Moussorgsky, Modeste** (Muhs-sorg'sky). Russian opera composer, 1839–1881. "Boris Godounov."

**Mozart, W. A.** (Mot'sart). One of the greatest German composers, 1756–91. Operas, symphonies, chamber music, piano works.

**Nageli, H. G.** Swiss music composer and publisher. Writer of well-known hymn tunes such as "Blest Be the Tie That Binds."

**Nessler, Victor.** German operatic composer, 1841–90. "Trumpeter of Sakkingen."

**Nevin, Ethelbert.** American composer of salon music, 1862–1901. Piano pieces, songs, "The Rosary," "Serenade," etc.

**Nicolai, Otto.** German opera composer and conductor, 1810–1849. "Merry Wives of Windsor."

**Offenbach, Jacques** (Of'fen-bahkh). French comic-opera composer, 1819–1880. "Tales of Hoffman."

**Olsen, Ole.** Norwegian composer, 1850–1927. "Serenade."

**Paderewski, Ignace** (Pahd-ref'ski). Polish pianist-composer, 1860–1941. "Minuet L'Antique."

**Palmgren, Selim.** Finnish composer and pianist, 1878– —. Many popular piano works such as "May-night."

**Parry, Joseph.** Welsh opera composer, 1841–1903. "Blodwen."

**Payne, John Howard.** American dramatist, 1792–1852. "Home Sweet Home" (words).

**Pierné, Gabriel** (Pyair-nay'). French composer, 1863–1937. "Serenade."

**Planquette, Robert** (Plon-ket'). French comic-opera composer, 1848–1903. "Chimes of Normandy."

**Pleyel, Ignaz** (Play-el'). German conductor, piano manufacturer and composer, 1757–1831. "Pleyel's Hymn."

**Poldini, Eduard** (Poll-dee'nee). Hungarian composer of light piano music, 1869– —. "Dancing Doll."

**Ponchielli, Amilcare** (Pon-ki-el'lee). Italian operatic composer. 1834–86. "La Gioconda."

**Prokofieff, Serge** (Proh-koff'ee-eff). Russian modernist composer, 1891– —. Orchestral works, operas, piano music, "Peter and the Wolf."

**Puccini, Giacomo** (Poo-chee'nee). Italian opera composer, 1858–1924. "Le Villi," "La Boheme," "La Tosca," "Madame Butterfly," etc.

**Rachmaninoff, Sergei** (Rahk-mahn'ee-nof). Russian pianist-composer, 1873–1943. "Prelude in C Sharp Minor."

**Raff, Joachim.** German composer, 1822–82. Piano compositions.

**Rameau, J. P.** (Rah-mo'). French composer, 1683–1764. "Le Tambourin."

**Ravel, Maurice** (Rah-vehl'). French composer, 1875–1937. "Bolero," "Pavane," etc.

**Reading, John.** English organist-composer, born early part of seventeenth century, died in 1692. Supposed to have written "Adeste Fideles" (O Come, All Ye Faithful).

**Rimsky-Korsakow, Nicholas.** Russian composer, 1844–1908. "Shehérazade," "Le Coq d'Or."

**Rodney, Paul.** English composer of sacred songs such as "Cavalry."

**Roeder, Martin** (Ray'der). German composer, 1851–95. "Love's Dreamland" Waltzes.

**Root, George F.** American composer, 1820–95. "Battle Cry of Freedom," "Vacant Chair," etc.

**Rossini, Gioacchino** (Ros-see'nee). Italian operatic composer, 1792–1868. "William Tell" Overture.

**Rubinstein, Anton** (Roo'bin-stein). Russian pianist-composer, 1829–94. "Melody in F."

**Saint-Saëns, Camille** (San'sans). French composer, 1835–1922. Orchestral and piano compositions.

**Sankey, Ira D.** American evangelist and hymn composer, 1840–1908. "Ninety and Nine."

**Scarlatti, Domenico** (Skar-laht'ti). Italian harpsichord (antique style of piano) player and composer, 1685–1757. Various piano pieces and operas.

**Scharwenka, Philipp** (Shar-ven'ka). German composer, 1847–1917. Piano pieces.

**Scharwenka, Xaver** (Shar-ven'ka). German composer, 1850–1924. Polish dances.

**Schertzinger, Victor L.** American composer of light music, 1890–1941. "Marcheta."

**Schubert, Franz** (Schoo'-behr). German composer, 1797–1828. "Ständchen" (Serenade), "Ave Maria," etc.

**Schumann, Robert** (Schoo'mann). German composer, 1810–56. "Träumerei," "Romance in F Sharp," etc.

**Schütt, Edward** (Shuett). Russian composer, 1856–1933. "A la Bien Aimée," "Romance." etc.

**Schytte, Ludwig** (Sheet-teh'). Danish composer, 1848–1909. Light piano pieces.

**Scriabin, Alexander** (Skreeah'bin). Russian composer, 1872–1915. Orchestral music, piano pieces.

**Shostakovitch, Dmitri.** (Shohs-ta-koh'vitch). Soviet-Russian composer, 1906– —. Symphonies, operas, piano pieces.

**Sibelius, Jean.** Finnish symphonic composer, 1865– —. "Valse Triste" and "Finlandia."

**Silcher, Friedrich** (Zil'-yher). German song composer, 1789–1860. "The Loreley."

**Sinding, Christian.** Norwegian composer, 1856–1941. "Rustle of Spring."

**Smetana, Bedrich.** Bohemian operatic composer, 1824–84. "Bartered Bride."

**Spendiarow, Alexander.** Russian composer, 1871–1928. Piano music.

**Stojowski, Sigismond.** Polish pianist and composer, 1870– —. Several piano compositions.

**Straus, Oscar** (Strous). Viennese light-opera composer, 1870– —. "The Waltz Dream."

**Strauss, Johann, Jr.** (Strowss). Viennese composer, known as the "Waltz King," 1825–99. "Beautiful Blue Danube" Waltzes.

**Strauss, Richard** (Strowss). German composer, ultra-Wagnerian in form and harmony, 1864– —. "Salome" and "Thus Spake Zarathustra," etc.

**Stravinsky, Igor** (Strah-vin'skee). Russian modernist composer, 1882– —. Orchestral works, ballets, "The Firebird," etc.

**Sullivan, Sir Arthur.** English composer of comic operas and sacred songs, 1842–1900. "Pinafore," "Mikado," "Lost Chord."

**Suppé, Franz Von** (Soop-peh'). German comic-opera composer, 1819–95. "Poet and Peasant" Overture.

**Szalit, Paula.** Scandinavian pianist, composer of many popular piano numbers.

**Templeton, Alec.** Blind English-born American pianist, composer, and parodist, 1910– —. "Mozart Matriculates," "A Lullaby," etc.

**Thomas, Ambroise** (Toe'ma). French operatic composer, 1811–96. "Mignon."

**Thomé, Francis** (Toe'may). French teacher, critic, and composer, 1850–1909. "Simple Aveu."

**Tosti, Paolo.** Italian singing-teacher and vocal composer, 1846–1916. "Goodbye," "Beauty's Eyes," etc.

**Trotére, Henry** (Tro-tare'). English song composer (Henry Trotter), 1855–1912. "In Old Madrid."

**Tschaikowsky, Peter** (Chi-koff'ski). Russian Composer, 1840–93. "Chant Sans Paroles," "Romeo & Juliet"; Piano Concertos; Symphonies.

**Verdi, Giuseppe** (Vair'de). Italian operatic composer, 1813–1901. "Rigoletto," "Il Trovatore," "Aïda," etc.

**Wagner, Richard** (Vahg'ner). The greatest opera (music drama) composer of all time, 1813–83. "Lohengrin," "Tannhäuser," "Tristan and Isolde," etc.

**Waldteufel, Emil** (Vahld-toi'fel). German composer of graceful dance music, 1837–1915. "Estudiantina," "Très Jolie" Waltzes, etc.

**Wallace, William Vincent.** Irish operatic composer, 1812–65. "Maritana."

**Waller, Thomas** (Fats). American Negro pianist and composer of popular music, 1904–1943. "A Handful of Keys."

**Waring, Tom.** American song-composer, 1902– —. "Ol' Darkie, Ol' Mule."

**Webb, George James.** English-born American composer of hymn-tunes, 1803–1887. "Stand Up for Jesus."

**Webbe, Samuel.** English church-music composer, 1740–1816. "Come Ye Disconsolate."

**Weber, Carl Maria von** (Vay'ber). German composer, founder of the romantic school of opera, 1786–1826. "Der Freischütz."

**Wesley, Samuel.** English organist and church-music composer, brother of Charles Wesley, 1766–1837. Composed several well-known hymn tunes.

**Work, Henry C.** American composer, entirely self-taught, 1832–84. "Marching Through Georgia."

**Youferoff, Serge.** Russian composer of piano music, 1864– —.

**Yradier, Sebastian** (Ee-rah-di-air'). Spanish composer, 1809–65. "La Paloma."

**Ziehrer, Carl.** German comic-opera and dance-music composer, 1843–1922. "Vienna Maidens" Waltzes.

# A LIST OF IMPORTANT MUSICAL TERMS AND EXPRESSIONS

*Compiled by Albert E. Wier*

The following brief list of musical terms and expressions is designed to define concisely but plainly such musical terms, expressions, and abbreviations as are used in the music pages of "The Scribner Radio Music Library." It is merely intended as a ready reference list in which the meaning of an unfamiliar term may be readily ascertained. The mark ′ indicates the accented syllable of each word.

**Aban′don.** Without restraint.

**A′bendlied.** Evening song.

**Accel.** Abbreviation for "Acceleran′-do."

**Acceleran′do.** Increasing the speed.

**Ac′cent.** The emphasis of certain tones over others.

**Acciden′tals.** Occasional sharps, flats, or naturals placed before notes.

**Accomp.** Abbreviation for "Accompaniment."

**Accom′paniment.** The musical background to the principal part.

**Acous′tics.** The science of sound.

**Ada′gio.** Slow, faster than lar′go and slower than adan′te.

**Ad Lib.** Abbreviation for "Ad Lib′i-tum."

**Ad Lib′itum.** At will, play to suit your own idea of the time, or play or omit, according to your taste.

**Agita′to.** Agitated, hurried.

**Air.** A short melody, with or without words.

**Al′bum Leaf.** A short, simple piece.

**Al Fine.** To the end.

**Allargan′do.** Growing louder and slower.

**Allegret′to.** Cheerfully and quickly.

**Alle′gro.** Quickly, vivaciously.

**Alle′gro Agita′to.** Quickly and with agitation.

**Alle′gro Con Bri′o.** Quickly with brilliancy.

**Alle′gro Con Fuo′co.** Quickly and full of fire.

**Alle′gro Modera′to.** Moderately quick.

**Alle′gro non Trop′po.** Not too quickly.

**Alle′gro Viva′ce.** Very rapidly.

**Allelu′ia.** "Praise the Lord."

**Al Se′gno.** "Go back to the sign," which means that the player must return to the sign :S: previously marked above some bar of the composition, and play from that measure to the word "Fine" or the mark ⌒.

**Al′to.** The female voice part next below the soprano.

**Am′ateur.** One who loves music and is proficient without practising it as a profession.

**Amen′.** "So be it." The usual ending of hymns, psalms, etc.

**Amoro′so.** Tenderly, affectionately.

**Anal′ysis.** The harmonic or structural dissection of a musical composition.

**Andan′te.** In a moderate tempo, with expression and grace.

**Andan′te Canta′bile.** Slowly and in a singing style.

**Andan′te Con Mo′to.** With an easy motion.

**Andan′te ma non Trop′po.** Not too slow.

**Andan′te Quasi Allegret′to.** Nearly as fast as "Allegretto."

**Andanti′no.** Less slow than "Andante."

**Anfang.** The beginning.

**An′gelus.** A bell rung in Catholic countries for prayers at morning, noon, and evening.

**Anima′to.** With life and spirit, animatedly.

**An′them.** A sacred vocal composition, words usually selected from the Bible.

**A po′co.** Gradually.

**A po′co pi′u Len′to.** A little slower.

**A po′co pi′u Mos′so.** A little quicker.

**Appassiona′to.** Passionately.

**Appoggiatu′ra.** A grace note or embellishment.

**Arabesque′.** A musical composition of ornamental character.

**A′ria.** A song or air, usually in an opera or oratorio.

**Arpeg′gio.** The notes of a chord played quickly one after the other.

**Arrangement.** The selection or adaptation of a composition from one form to another.

**Articula′tion.** Clarity of utterance in speaking or singing.

**Artist.** One who excels in musical performance.

**Assa′i.** Very, extremely.

**A Tem′po.** In time.

**Attack.** Method of beginning a musical phrase.

**Aubade′.** Morning music.

**Aus′drucksvoll.** Expressively.

**Ballad.** A short, simple song.

**Bal′let.** A dancing pantomime, with musical accompaniment.

**Band.** A number of instrumental performers playing together.

**Bar.** The dividing line between two musical measures.

**Bar′carolle.** The song of Venetian boatmen.

**Bar′itone.** The male voice which is intermediate between tenor and bass.

**Bass.** The lowest male voice; the lowest part in a musical composition.

**Bass Clef.** The F clef, on the fourth line of the musical staff.

**Bat′on.** The stick used by the conductor of an orchestra or band.

**Beglei′tung.** An accompaniment.

**Ben Marca′to.** Well marked or accented.

**Ben Tenu′to.** Well sustained.

**Ber′ceuse.** A cradle-song.

**Bluet′te.** A short, brilliant piece.

**Bole′ro.** A lively Spanish dance.

**Bourree′.** An old French dance.

**Brillan′te.** Brilliantly.

**Brindi′si.** A drinking song.

**Cabalet′ta.** A simple melodic composition.

**Cachu′cha.** A popular Spanish dance.

**Ca′dence.** A close in melody or harmony, effecting a division into periods, or bringing it to a close.

**Caden′za.** A cadence or ornamental passage introduced near the end of a composition.

**Cake-walk.** A species of dance peculiar to the Southern negro.

**Calan′do.** Gradually diminishing in tone and growing slower in time.

**Canta′bile.** In a singing style.

**Canta′ta.** A secular or sacred poem set to music.

**Cantile′na.** A melody or air of a musical composition.

**Canzonet′ta.** A little song.

**Capricciet′to.** A short form of capriccio.

**Capric′cio.** A fanciful musical composition.

**Caprice′.** See "Capriccio."

**Car′ol.** A song of joy or devotion.

**Cavati′na.** A short simple song, or an instrumental composition of a song-like character.

**Chaconne′.** A series of variations in which the theme is merely a succession of chords which serves as a harmonic basis of each variation.

**Chamber Music.** Instrumental duets, trios, quartets, etc.

**Chan′son.** A simple vocal or instrumental composition.

**Chant.** A simple melody.

**Chantant′.** In a melodious or singing style.

**Characteristic Piece.** A musical composition with a distinct character.

**Chorale′.** A hymn-tune of the German Protestant Church.

**Chord.** The union of two or more tones played at one time.

**Chor′ister.** A singer in, or leader of, a choir.

**Cho′rus.** The refrain of a song. Also a company of singers.

**Chromat′ic.** Proceeding by semitones.

**Chromat′ic Signs.** Accidentals, such as sharps flats, or naturals.

**Clas′sical Music.** Music which has been accepted as standard.

**Clav′ichord.** See "Klavier."

**Clavier.** The French word for keyboard. See "Klavier."

**Clef.** A character used to determine the names and pitch of the notes on a musical staff.

**Clef, Bass.** The characters at the commencement of the staff, which indicate the names and pitch of the notes. The F clef.

**Clef, Treble.** The G clef, used in the upper staff of the piano score.

**Co′da.** The end of a piece, usually a few bars added in order to conclude a musical composition more effectually.

**Colla Vo′ce.** Follow the voice.

**Commo′do.** Easily, composedly.

**Com′pass.** The range of notes or sounds possessed by any musical instrument or the human voice.

**Compo′ser.** The writer of a musical composition.

**Composi′tion.** Any musical production.

**Con Amo′re.** With tenderness.

**Con An′ima.** With animation.

**Con Brav′ura.** With brilliance.

**Con Bri′o.** With spirit.

**Con Calo′re.** With warmth.

**Concer′to.** An elaborate instrumental solo piece with orchestral accompaniment, usually in three distinct or connected parts.

**Con Dolo′re.** With pathos.

**Conduc′tor.** The leader of an orchestra or chorus.

**Con Esp.** Abbreviation for "Con Espressione."

**Con Espressio′ne.** With expression.

**Conser′vatory.** A school or academy of music, where every branch of the art is taught.

**Consola′tion.** A musical composition of soothing character.

**Con′sonance.** An accord of sounds agreeable to the ear.

**Cresc.** Abbreviation for "Crescendo."

**Crescen′do.** Increase in power of tone.

**Crescen′do al diminuen′do.** Increase and then diminish the tone.

**D. C.** Abbreviation for "Da Capo."

**Da Ca′po.** From the beginning.

**Da Ca'po al Fi'ne.** Return to the beginning and play as far as the word "Fine."

**Da Ca'po Sin'al Se'gno.** Return to the beginning, play as far as the sign, then play the "Coda."

**D. S.** Abbreviation for "Dal Segno."

**Dal Se'gno.** Repeat from the sign :S:

**Dal Se'gno Alla Fîne.** Repeat from the sign :S: to the word "Fine."

**Dead March.** A funeral march.

**Deci'so.** In a decided manner.

**Decresc.** Abbreviation for "Decrescen'do."

**Decrescen'do.** Gradually diminish in power of tone.

**Delibera'to.** Deliberately.

**Delica'to.** Delicately.

**Diato'nic.** Proceeding in the order of the degrees of the natural scale.

**Diato'nic Scale.** The natural scale as represented by the white notes of the piano keyboard. There is, of course, a corresponding scale in every key.

**Dim.** Abbreviation for "Diminuen'do."

**Diminuen'do.** Decreasing gradually the power of the tone.

**Dirge.** A slow composition for use at a funeral or commemorative occasion.

**Dis'sonance.** A discord, opposite of "Consonance."

**Divertimen'to.** A short light composition.

**Dol'ce.** Sweetly and softly.

**Dol'ce e Canta'bile.** Sweetly in a singing style.

**Dolen'te.** Mournfully.

**Dotted Double Bar.** Dots *before* a double bar indicate that the preceding strain is to be repeated; *after* a double bar that the strain which follows is to be repeated. Dots on both sides indicate both styles of repetition.

**Douce'ment.** Sweetly and softly.

**Doxol'ogy.** A song of praise at the close of a religious service.

**Elegan'te.** Elegant.

**El'egie.** A funeral song or mournful poem.

**Embel'lishments.** Ornamental notes added to make a melody more effective.

**Em'phasis.** Particular accent on any one note, indicated by a sign.

**Ener'gico.** Vigorous, forcible.

**Ensem'ble Music.** Concerted music, played by a group of instrumentalists or vocalists.

**Entr'ac'te.** Music played between the acts of a drama or opera.

**Espress.** Abbreviation for "Espressivo."

**Espressi'vo.** Expressive.

**E'tude.** A study or exercise for the development of technique.

**Execu'tion.** Vocal or instrumental technical dexterity.

**Ex'ercise.** A composition aimed to develop technique.

**Expression.** Variations of tempo, phrasing, accent, volume of tone, etc., which render a performance of music expressive and meaningful.

**F.** Abbreviation for "Forte."

**FF.** Abbreviation for "Fortissimo."

**FFF.** Abbreviation for "Fortississimo."

**Facilement'.** With facility.

**Fandan'go.** A lively Spanish dance.

**Fan'tasie.** An imaginative musical composition.

**F Clef.** The bass clef.

**Festi'vo.** Merrily, gayly.

**Fina'le.** The last part of an opera or the last movement of a sonata or symphony.

**Fingering.** The method of applying the fingers to the keys, strings, or holes of different instruments.

**Flat.** A musical sign which, if placed in front of a note, lowers it a semitone in pitch.

**Form.** The architecture or structure of musical composition.

**For'te.** Loud.

**Fortis'simo.** Very loud.

**Fortissis'simo.** As loud as possible.

**Forz.** Abbreviation for "Forzando."

**Forzan'do.** Forcing, or forced.

**Forza'to.** See "Forzando."

**Früh'lingslied.** A spring song.

**Fugue'.** A classical form of musical composition.

**Fune'bre.** Funereal, mournful.

**Funeral March.** A march in slow tempo, for use at a funeral.

**Fuo'co.** Fire, passion.

**Furio'so.** Furious, mad.

**Gai'ement.** Gayly, merrily.

**Gal'op.** A quick dance.

**Gavotte'.** A stately and genial dance.

**G Clef.** The treble clef.

**Genti'le.** Elegant, graceful.

**Gioco'so.** Sportively.

**Glissan'do.** In a gliding manner, accomplished on the piano, by drawing the fingers rapidly over the keyboard.

**Grace Note.** An ornamental note or embellishment.

**Grandio'so.** Grand, noble.

**Grave.** A slow, solemn movement.

**Gregorian Chant.** The liturgical chant of the Roman Catholic Church.

**Habane'ra.** A slow Spanish dance.

**Hallelu'jah.** "Praise Ye the Lord."

**Har'mony.** The art of combining sounds into chords.

**Hex'antanz.** A fanciful composition depicting a witches' dance.

**Hold.** A sign ⌒ indicating that the period of sound or rest is to be prolonged.

**Humoreske'.** A playful musical composition.

**Hymn.** A religious song of praise.

**I'dyl.** A musical composition in pastoral style.

**Impromp'tu.** A fanciful composition.

**Im'provise.** To sing, play, or compose music at will.

**In'terlude.** The intermediate strain between the verses of a hymn or song.

**Intermez'zo.** A detached piece introduced between the acts of an opera. Also used as the title for any light, graceful composition.

**In'terval.** The difference in pitch between two musical tones.

**Intro.** Abbreviation for "Introduction."

**Introduc'tion.** The first measures in a musical composition which prepare one for the main part.

**Jig.** A light, brisk dance, popular in Ireland.

**Klavi'er.** The German word for pianoforte, but also applied to those keyboard instruments which were forerunners of the modern piano: clavichord, harpsichord, etc.

**Lagrimo'so.** Tearful.

**Lamentan'do.** Lamenting.

**Land'ler.** A country dance.

**Lang'sam.** Slowly.

**Larghet'to.** Not quite as slow as "Largo."

**Lar'go.** Solemn and slow.

**Lar'go ma non Trop'po.** Slow but not too much so.

**Leg.** Abbreviation for "Legato."

**Lega'to.** In a smooth manner, slurred.

**Lega'to Touch.** Sliding the fingers on and off the keys of the piano, holding down each note until the next is played.

**Legere'ment.** Lightly, nimbly.

**Leggier'o.** Light and swift.

**Lent.** Slow.

**Lentemen'te.** Slowly.

**Len'to.** Slow.

**L. H.** Abbreviation for "Left Hand."

**Libret'to.** The text of an opera, oratorio, etc.

**Lie'beslied.** A love-song.

**Lied.** A song or ballad.

**Lied'er.** Songs.

**Lied'er Ohne Wor'te.** Songs without words.

**L'istes'so Tempo.** The same tempo.

**Loure.** A slow, dignified dance.

**Lul'laby.** A cradle-song.

**Mad'rigal.** An elaborate vocal composition in three or more parts.

**Maesto'so.** Majestic, dignified.

**Ma'jor.** Greater, applied to intervals and scales.

**Marc.** Abbreviation for "Marcato."

**Marca'to.** Strongly accented.

**March.** A movement especially adapted for marching.

**Marseillaise'.** A French national air.

**Mass.** A sacred vocal composition.

**Mas'tersingers.** A class of poet-musicians in Germany.

**Mazur'ka.** A lively Polish dance.

**Medita'tion.** A religious composition usually instrumental.

**Melodieux'.** Melodiously.

**Melody.** A succession of tones forming a combination pleasing in sound and rhythm to the ear.

**Me'no.** Less.

**Me'no Mosso.** Slower.

**Menu'et.** See "Minuet."

**Method.** A system of instruction.

**Met'ronome.** An instrument for measuring the duration of notes.

**M. M.** Abbreviation for "Maelzel's Metronome."

**Met'ronome Marks.** Figures placed at the beginning of a piece of music, referring to the metronome.

**M. F.** Abbreviation for "Mezzo Forte."

**Mezzo For'te.** Moderately loud.

**M. P.** Abbreviation for "Mezzo Piano."

**Mezzo Pia'no.** Moderately soft.

**Mig'non.** Dainty, petite, charming.

**Mi'nor.** Smaller, applied to intervals and scales.

**Minuet'.** A slow, stately dance.

**Misere're.** "Have mercy," a prayer.

**Misterio'so.** Mysteriously.

**Mit Bewe'gung.** With movement.

**Mo'bile.** Movable, changeable.

**Mod.** Abbreviation for "Moderato."

**Modera'to.** Moderately.

**Modula'tion.** Transition from one musical key to another.

**Morceau'.** A choice musical composition.

**Mor'dent.** A musical embellishment.

**Mos'so.** Motion or movement.

**Mo'tive.** The theme of a musical composition.

**Mo'to.** Motion, movement.

**Mo'to Perpet'uo.** Perpetual motion.

**National Music.** The songs or dances characteristic of a nation.

**No'bile.** Noble, impressive.

**Noc'turne.** A dreamy, romantic composition.

**Noël.** A Christmas carol or hymn.

**Non.** "No."

**Novellette'.** An instrumental composition of romantic character.

**Obbliga'to.** A part added to a composition, in addition to the usual accompaniment.

**Ode.** An air or song.

**Oh'ne.** "Without."

**Op'era.** A drama or comedy set to music.

**O'pus.** The work of a composer indicated in the order of its inception or publication.

**Or'chestra.** A collection of string and wind instrument performers playing together.

**Ornamen'tal Notes.** Grace notes added to the regular notes of the measure.

**O'verture.** The preliminary instrumental portion of an opera. Sometimes a separate composition.

**Pan'tomime.** A wordless play with musical accompaniment.

**Par'aphrase.** A transcription or special arrangement of a musical composition.

**Part.** The music for each individual voice or instrument.

**Part-Songs.** Songs written in parts for different voices.

**Pas'sage.** Any phrase or short portion of a melody.

**Pas'sion Music.** Compositions of sacred character depicting the sufferings of Christ.

**Pastorale'.** A composition suggestive of country life.

**Pathetique'.** Pathetic.

**Patrol'.** A composition which imitates the approach and departure of a military body.

**Pav'ane.** A stately, slow dance.

**Ped.** Abbreviation for "Pedal."

**Ped'als.** The mechanism at the base of a piano which enables the performer to play with varying degrees of tone.

**Perdendo'si.** Gradually dying away.

**Pe'riod.** A complete musical sentence containing two or more phrases.

**Phan'tasie.** See "Fantasia."

**Phrase.** A short musical sentence.

**Piace're (A).** At pleasure.

**P.** Abbreviation for "Piano."

**Piano.** Soft.

**Pp.** Abbreviation for "Pianissimo."

**Pianissimo.** Very soft.

**PPP.** Abbreviation for "Pianississimo."

**Pianississimo.** As soft as possible.

**Pitch.** The location of a musical sound in the musical scale.

**Pi'u.** More.

**Pi'u Alle'gro.** More quickly.

**Pi'u For'te.** Louder.

**Pi'u Len'to.** More slowly.

**Pi'u Mos'so.** More quickly.

**Pi'u Pia'no.** More softly.

**Pi'u Pres'to.** More rapidly.

**Pi'u Vi'vo.** More lively.

**Pizzica'to.** In violin, or other bowed instrument, playing, plucked rather than bowed.

**Placi'do.** Calm, quiet.

**Plus.** More.

**Plus Anime'.** With more animation.

**Plus Len'tement.** More slowly.

**Po'co.** Little.

**Po'co Ada gio.** A little slower.

**Po'co Alle'gro.** A little faster.

**Po'co Anima'to.** A little more animated.

**Po'co a po'co.** By degrees.

**Po'co a po'co Crescen'do.** Gradually louder and louder.

**Po'co a po'co Diminuen'do.** Gradually softer and softer.

**Po'co pi'u Mos'so.** A little faster.

**Pol'ka.** A lively Bohemian dance.

**Pol'ka Mazur'ka.** A slow dance, in ¾ time, accented on the last or third beat.

**Polonaise'.** A Polish dance of stately character.

**Pre'lude.** A short composition of an introductory character.

**Pres'to.** Quickly, rapidly.

**Pres'to Assai'.** Very quick.

**Pres'to ma non Trop'po.** Not too quick.

**Priere'.** A prayer.

**Pri'ma Don'na.** Principal female singer in an opera.

**Pri'mo.** The word placed over the part for the upper player in piano-duet arrangements.

**Pro'gram Mu'sic.** Compositions which are inspired by, or suggestive of, scenes or stories which the music attempts to describe.

**Pro'logue.** The instrumental or vocal introduction to an opera.

**Psalm.** A sacred song or hymn.

**Quadrille'.** A French dance in five consecutive parts.

**Qua'si.** "Like."

**Qua'si Allegret'to.** Like an "Allegretto."

**Qua'si Andan'te.** "Like an "Adante."

**Qua'si Pres'to.** Like a "Presto."

**Qua'si un Fanta'sia.** Like a "Fantasy."

**Rall.** Abbreviation for "Rallentando."

**Rallentan'do.** Gradually slower.

**Rapi'do.** Rapid.

**Rec'itative.** Musical declamation.

**Re'dowa.** A Bohemian dance.

**Reel.** A lively Scotch dance.

**Refrain'.** The chorus of a song.

**Religio'so.** Religiously.

**Repeat Marks.** Marks indicating that a certain portion or portions of a piece are to be immediately played over again.

**Re'pertoire.** The operas well known by an opera company; the compositions well known by an artist or musical amateur.

**Re'quiem.** A musical service in honor of the dead.

**R. H.** Abbreviation for "Right Hand."

**Rhap'sody.** A fanciful musical composition.

**Risolu'to.** Resolutely, boldly.

**Ritard.** Abbreviation for "Ritardando."

**Ritardan'do.** Holding back the time.

**Riten. or Rit.** Abbreviation for "Ritenuto."

**Ritenu'to.** Held back.

**Ro'mance.** An imaginative vocal or instrumental composition.

**Ron'do.** A vocal or instrumental composition containing one constantly recurring theme.

**Ruba'to.** Taking part of the rightful time-duration of one note and giving it to another.

**Salterel'la.** An Italian dance in quick time.

**Saraban'de.** A slow, grave dance.

**Scale.** The succession of musical tones on which music is constructed.

**Scherz.** Abbreviation for "Scherzando."

**Scherzan'do.** In a playful manner.

**Scher'zo.** A playful composition.

**Schnell.** Quickly, rapidly.

**Schot'tische.** A pouplar modern dance.

**Schlum'merlied.** A slumber-song.

**Score.** The instrumental or vocal (or both) parts of a composition written on separate lines which are placed one under the other, so that the measures of every part may be read simultaneously by the conductor.

**Score (Piano).** A score in which the orchestral parts of an opera, etc., have been arranged so as to be played for piano solo.

**Secon'do.** The word placed over the part for the lower player in piano-duet arrangements.

**Sec'ular Music.** Ordinary music not sacred in character.

**Se'gno.** A sign :S: indicating a return to some previous part of the composition.

**Semitone.** The half of a whole tone, the smallest interval of the chromatic scale.

**Semp.** Abbreviation for "Sempre."

**Sem'pre.** Always, ever to a greater degree.

**Sem'pre For'te.** Ever loud.

**Sem'pre Lega'to.** Ever legato.

**Sem'pre Pia'no.** Ever piano.

**Sem'pre Pi'u For'te.** Ever louder.

**Sem'pre Pi'u Pres'to.** Ever faster.

**Sem'pre Ritardan'do.** Ever slower.

**Sem'pre Stacca'to.** Ever staccato.

**Sentimen'to.** With sentiment.

**Sen'za Re'plica.** Without repeat.

**Serenata.** A serenade.

**Sextette'.** A composition for six voices.

**SFZ.** Abbreviation for "Sforzando."

**Sforzan'do, Sforza'to.** With a sudden accent on a single note or chord.

**Sharp.** A musical sign, which if placed in front of a note, raises it a semitone.

**Sig'nature.** The name given the sharps or flats of any key.

**Signs.** Various symbols indicating certain details of musical performance.

**So'loist.** One who performs a vocal or instrumental composition alone or with instrumental accompaniment.

**Sona'ta.** An instrumental composition, usually containing three or four movements.

**Sonati'na.** A short, easy sonata.

**Song.** A vocal number.

**Song without Words.** Short, melodic instrumental composition.

**Sono'rous.** Rich in musical sound.

**Sospiran'do.** Sighing.

**Sost.** Abbreviation for "Sostenuto."

**Sostenu'to.** Sustained.

**Spinet.** An older form of the modern piano.

**Stacc.** Abbreviation for "Staccato."

**Stacca'to.** Detached playing of notes.

**Staff.** The five lines on which notes are written.

**Ständ'chen.** A serenade.

**Stan'za.** The separate verses of a song or hymn.

**Step.** A degree upon the musical staff.

**String.** Abbreviation for "Stringendo."

**Stringen'do.** Accelerating the time.

**String Quartet.** A combination of four stringed instruments such as violins, violas, cellos, etc. Also the name of a composition for same.

**Style.** The manner in which a composition is written.

**Suite.** A series of musical movements or pieces.

**Sym'phony.** An orchestra composition in several parts.

**Tarantel'la.** A swift Italian dance.

**Tech'nique.** The mechanical part of playing a musical instrument.

**Tem'perament.** The individual power of musical feeling in an artist or musical amateur.

**Tem'po.** Musical time.

**Tem. 1°.** Abbreviation for "Tempo Primo."

**Tem'po Pri'mo.** First or original time as marked on a piece.

**Ten.** Abbreviation for "Tenuto."

**Ten'uto.** Sustained, held.

**Theme.** The melody or tune of a piece.

**Time.** The measure of sounds in respect to their relative duration.

**Time Sig'nature.** The indication of the time (such as ¼) at the beginning of a piece.

**Tone.** A sound of definite pitch.

**Touch.** The method of striking the keys of a piano or organ.

**Transcrip'tion.** A special arrangement of a musical composition for some instrument for which it was not originally intended.

**Transpose'.** To remove from one musical key to another.

**Träu'merei.** A dreamy musical composition.

**Trau'rig.** Sadly.

**Trem.** Abbreviation for "Tremolo."

**Tre'molo.** Reiterating a note or chord combination with great rapidity.

**Tres.** Very.

**Tres Anime'.** Very lively.

**Tres Fort.** Very loud.

**Tres Lente.** Very slow.

**Tres Pia'no.** Very soft.

**Tres Vi'te.** Very quick.

**Tri'ad.** The common chord, consisting of a note with its third and fifth (for instance C–E–G).

**Tr.** Abbreviation for "Trill."

**Trill.** The rapid alternation of a note and the next note above, as long as the time of the first note endures.

**Tri'o.** A composition for three instruments; also the second part of a minuet, march, etc.

**Turn.** A musical embellishment, made up of the note above and the note below the principal note.

**Two-Step.** A popular American dance in ⅜ time.

**Tyrolienne'.** A song or dance used in the Tyrol.

**Valse.** A waltz.

**Var.** Abbreviation for "Variation."

**Varia'tion.** The repetition of a theme in a new form while preserving the original melodic notes.

**Varsovienne'.** A dance in moderate ¾ time.

**Velo'ce.** Swiftly.

**Vif.** Lively, briskly.

**Vigoro'so.** Vigorously.

**Viva'ce.** Lively, vivaciously.

**Vi'vo.** Animated.

**Volks–Lied.** A national song.

**Vor'spiel.** Prelude, introduction.

**Waltz.** An animated dance in ¾ time, originating in Germany.

# FOREWORD TO
# THE COMPLETE INDEX

THE following complete index to "The Scribner Radio Music Library" is primarily an alphabetical arrangement by titles of all the compositions, both instrumental and vocal, in the entire series of nine volumes. The titles of piano compositions are printed in Roman type and the titles of vocal numbers in italics. This arrangement will be found very convenient when you desire to ascertain whether a certain composition, either vocal or instrumental, is contained in the "Library." Instead of looking through the indexes of the different volumes, merely look it up in the complete index which will give you the volume and the page number if the composition is in the work.

For your convenience in ascertaining what compositions by some of the most noted composers, such as Bach, Beethoven, Grieg, etc., are contained in the "Library," most of these composers' names have been listed alphabetically, with such of their compositions as are in the volumes indexed under their names. This has not been done in the case of individual composers of lesser note, as the index would then become too cumbersome.

The titles of all operas from which selections or songs have been included in the "Library" are indexed alphabetically, and under each of these titles will be found the names of the individual numbers. For example, if one wishes the "Toreador Song" from the opera "Carmen," he will find it indexed under the title "Toreador Song," and also under the title of the opera.

# A COMPLETE INDEX TO

# THE SCRIBNER RADIO MUSIC LIBRARY

| | | | VOL. | PAGE |
|---|---|---|---|---|
| A.D.MDCXX (Sea Pieces), Op. 55, No. 3 | MacDowell | | IX— | 59 |
| Abide With Me | Monk | | VII— | 255 |
| Abraham | MacGimsey | | IX— | 194 |
| Adagio Cantabile ("Pathetique" Sonata) | Beethoven | | I— | 30 |
| Adagio ("Moonlight" Sonata) | Beethoven | | I— | 21 |
| Adagio (Octet, Op. 166) | Schubert | | I— | 100 |
| Adios (Rhumba) | Madriguera | | IX— | 136 |
| After the Ball | Harris | | IX— | 219 |
| Agnus Dei | Bizet | | IX— | 172 |
| Ah! I Have Sighed to Rest Me (Il Trovatore) | Verdi | | VII— | 79 |
| Ah! So Pure (Martha) | Flotow | | VII— | 54 |
| **Aida** | | | | |
| Heav'nly Aïda | Verdi | | VII— | 10 |
| Selection | Verdi | | IV— | 6 |
| Air for the G String | Bach | | I— | 16 |
| A la bien-aimée, Op. 59, No. 2 | Schütt | | II— | 187 |
| **Albeniz, I.** | | | | |
| Tango | Albeniz | | III— | 14 |
| Alice Where Art Thou? | Ascher | | VIII— | 80 |
| Alla Mazurka | Nemerowsky | | III— | 152 |
| All God's Chillun Got Wings | Spiritual | | VII— | 198 |
| All Hail the Pow'r of Jesus' Name! | Holden | | VII— | 255 |
| All Through the Night | Welsh Song | | VIII— | 69 |
| Allerseelen (All Soul's Day) | Strauss | | IX— | 188 |
| Aloha Oe | Hawaiian Song | | VIII— | 117 |
| Always or Never (Waltzes) | Waldteufel | | VI— | 64 |
| Amaryllis | Ghys | | III— | 138 |
| America | Carey | | VIII— | 159 |
| America the Beautiful | Ward | | IX— | 236 |
| American Hymn, The | Keller | | IX— | 237 |
| **American Patriotic Songs.** See Vols. VIII and IX | | | | |
| Amor (Bolero) | Ruiz | | IX— | 139 |
| Andante Cantabile (Fifth Symphony) | Tschaikowsky | | II— | 218 |
| Andante Cantabile (Quartet, Op. 11) | Tschaikowsky | | II— | 226 |
| Andante Con Moto (Fifth Symphony) | Beethoven | | I— | 40 |
| Andante (Kreutzer Sonata) | Beethoven | | I— | 26 |
| Andante (Orfeo) | Gluck | | I— | 47 |
| Andante ("Surprise" Symphony) | Haydn | | I— | 76 |
| Andante Religioso | Thomé | | VII— | 111 |
| Andantino | Lemare | | VII— | 90 |
| An den Frühling, Op. 43, No. 6 | Grieg | | II— | 50 |
| Angel of Love (Waltzes) | Waldteufel | | VI— | 100 |
| Angel's Serenade | Braga | | VII— | 94 |
| Angelus, The | Massenet | | VII— | 122 |
| Anitra's Dance (Peer Gynt) | Grieg | | II— | 47 |
| Annie Laurie | Scott | | VIII— | 85 |
| Apache Dance (Valse Lente) | Hewitt | | VI— | 222 |
| **Arditi, Luigi** | | | | |
| Il Bacio (The Kiss) | Arditi | | IX— | 110 |
| Artist Life (Waltzes) | Strauss | | VI— | 21 |
| Ase's Death (Peer Gynt) | Grieg | | II— | 64 |
| At the Convent (Petite Suite) | Borodin | | IX— | 154 |
| Aufschwung (Soaring), Op. 12, No. 2 | Schumann | | I— | 206 |
| **Auber, D.** | | | | |
| Fra Diavolo (Selection) | Auber | | V— | 93 |
| **Audran, Ed.** | | | | |
| Mascot, The (Selection) | Audran | | V— | 98 |
| Olivette (Selection) | Audran | | V— | 104 |
| Auld Lang Syne | Scotch Song | | VIII— | 143 |
| Au Revoir (Waltzes) | Waldteufel | | VI— | 109 |
| Ave Maria | Gounod | | VII— | 128 |
| Ave Maria | Gounod | | VII— | 134 |
| Ave Maria | Mascagni | | VII— | 144 |
| Ave Maria | Schubert | | VII— | 126 |
| Ave Maria | Schubert | | IX— | 162 |
| **Bach, J. S.** | | | | |
| Air for the G String | Bach | | I— | 16 |
| Bourrée (Second Violin Sonata) | Bach | | I— | 18 |
| Gavotte (Sixth Violin Sonata) | Bach | | I— | 12 |
| Jesu, Joy of Man's Desiring | Bach | | IX— | 157 |
| Loure (Third 'Cello Suite) | Bach | | I— | 8 |
| Two Minuets (Second Partitur) | Bach | | I— | 10 |
| Prelude in C | Bach | | I— | 6 |

| | | | VOL. | PAGE |
|---|---|---|---|---|
| **Bach-Gounod** | | | | |
| Ave Maria | Bach-Gounod | | VII— | 128 |
| Ave Maria | Bach-Gounod | | VII— | 134 |
| Bacio, Il (The Kiss) | Arditi | | IX— | 110 |
| **Balfe, M. W.** | | | | |
| Bohemian Girl, The (Selection) | Balfe | | IV— | 17 |
| I Dreamt that I Dwelt in Marble Halls (Bohemian Girl) | Balfe | | VII— | 20 |
| **Ball, Ernest R.** | | | | |
| A Little Bit of Heaven | Ball | | IX— | 216 |
| **Ballets (Piano Selections).** See Vols. V and IX | | | | |
| Ballet Music (Rosamunde) | Schubert | | I— | 110 |
| Barcarolle, Op. 37, No. 6 (June) | Tschaikowsky | | II— | 240 |
| **Bartered Bride, The** | | | | |
| Selection | Smetana | | IV— | 12 |
| Battle Cry of Freedom, The | Root | | VIII— | 170 |
| Battle Hymn of the Republic | Steffe | | VIII— | 169 |
| Beautiful Dreamer | Foster | | VIII— | 204 |
| Beauty's Eyes | Tosti | | VIII— | 30 |
| **Beethoven, L. van** | | | | |
| Adagio ("Moonlight" Sonata) | Beethoven | | I— | 21 |
| Adagio Cantabile (Pathetique Sonata) | Beethoven | | I— | 30 |
| Andante Con Moto (Fifth Symphony) | Beethoven | | I— | 40 |
| Andante (Kreutzer Sonata) | Beethoven | | I— | 26 |
| Für Elise (Album Leaf) | Beethoven | | I— | 27 |
| Minuet in G | Beethoven | | I— | 24 |
| Rondo in C, Op. 51, No. 5 | Beethoven | | IX— | 14 |
| Scotch Dances (Ecossaisen) | Beethoven | | I— | 34 |
| Turkish March (Ruins of Athens) | Beethoven | | I— | 44 |
| Before Jehovah's Awful Throne | Venua | | VII— | 249 |
| **Beggar Student, The** | | | | |
| Selection | Millocker | | V— | 137 |
| Believe Me if All Those Endearing Young Charms | Moore | | VIII— | 100 |
| **Belle of New York, The** | | | | |
| Selection | Kerker | | IX— | 102 |
| **Bellini, V.** | | | | |
| Selection (Norma) | Bellini | | IV— | 31 |
| Ben Bolt | Kneass | | VIII— | 76 |
| Berceuse (Jocelyn) | Godard | | III— | 156 |
| Berceuse (Cradle Song) | Gottschalk | | IX— | 30 |
| Berceuse, Op. 13 | Ilyinsky | | II— | 68 |
| Berceuse, Op. 26, No. 7 | Schytte | | III— | 227 |
| Berceuse, Op. 3, No. 2 | Spendiarow | | II— | 211 |
| **Bizet, G.** | | | | |
| Agnus Dei | Bizet | | IX— | 172 |
| Habañera (Carmen) | Bizet | | VII— | 13 |
| Selection (Carmen) | Bizet | | IV— | 36 |
| Toreador Song (Carmen) | Bizet | | VII— | 16 |
| **Bland, James A.** | | | | |
| Carry Me Back to Old Virginny | Bland | | IX— | 230 |
| Oh! Dem Golden Slippers | Bland | | VIII— | 178 |
| Blessed Saviour, Thee I Love | Duffield | | VII— | 245 |
| Blest Be the Tie That Binds | Naegeli | | VII— | 254 |
| Blue Bells of Scotland, The | Scotch Folk Song | | VIII— | 99 |
| Blue Danube (Waltzes) | Strauss | | VI— | 6 |
| **Boccherini, L.** | | | | |
| Minuet in A | Boccherini | | I— | 88 |
| **Bohemian Girl, The** | | | | |
| Selection | Balfe | | IV— | 17 |
| **Bohm, C.** | | | | |
| Still as the Night | Bohm | | VIII— | 40 |
| Zingana, La | Bohm | | III— | 41 |
| **Boito, A.** | | | | |
| Mefistofele (Selection) | Boito | | IV— | 157 |
| Bonny Eloise | Thomas | | VIII— | 120 |
| **Boris Godounov** | | | | |
| Selection | Moussorgsky | | IV— | 22 |

| | VOL. | PAGE |
|---|---|---|
| **Borodin, A.** | | |
| At the Convent (Petite Suite) . . BORODIN | IX— | 154 |
| Nocturne (Petite Suite) . . . . BORODIN | IX— | 48 |
| Prince Igor (Selection) . . . . BORODIN | IV— | 174 |
| **Borowski, Felix** | | |
| Coquette, La . . . . . . BOROWSKI | III— | 220 |
| Valsetté . . . . . . . BOROWSKI | III— | 46 |
| Bourrée (Second Violin Sonata) . . BACH | I— | 18 |
| Bourrée (Armide) . . . . . GLUCK | I— | 51 |
| Bourrée in G . . . . . . HANDEL | I— | 60 |
| **Brahms, Johannes** | | |
| *Cradle Song* . . . . . . BRAHMS | VIII— | 21 |
| Hungarian Dance, No. 5 . . . BRAHMS | II— | 6 |
| Intermezzo, Op. 117, No. 1 . . BRAHMS | II— | 14 |
| Waltzes, Op. 39 (Selected) . . BRAHMS | II— | 10 |
| Bridal March (Lohengrin) . . . WAGNER | VII— | 120 |
| *Brightest and Best* . . . . WEBBE | VII— | 244 |
| Brooklyn Barcarolle . . . . DUKE | IX— | 118 |
| *Buffalo Gals* . . . . . . WHITE | IX— | 229 |
| *By an' By* . . . . . . SPIRITUAL | VII— | 208 |
| Bygone Days . . . . . . HARTHAN | III— | 109 |
| Cabaletta . . . . . . . LACK | III— | 190 |
| **Cadman, Charles Wakefield** | | |
| *Mistah Shakespeah* . . . . CADMAN | IX— | 196 |
| *Caissons Go Rolling Along, The* | | |
| (Artillery Song) . . . . GRUBER | IX— | 238 |
| *Calvary* . . . . . . . RODNEY | VII— | 138 |
| *Camptown Races* . . . . . FOSTER | VIII— | 197 |
| Canzonetta . . . . . . HOLLAENDER | III— | 176 |
| Caprice (Alceste) . . . . . GLUCK | I— | 54 |
| *Carmé* . . . . . . . ITALIAN SONG | VIII— | 106 |
| **Carmen** | | |
| *Habañera* . . . . . . BIZET | VII— | 13 |
| Selection . . . . . . BIZET | IV— | 36 |
| *Toreador Song* . . . . . BIZET | VII— | 16 |
| **Carmichael, Hoagy** | | |
| *Lazybones* . . . . . . CARMICHAEL AND | | |
| MERCER . | IX— | 234 |
| *Carol, Carol, Christians* . . . COXE | VII— | 234 |
| *Carry Me Back to Old Virginny* . . BLAND | IX— | 230 |
| **Casse-Noisette (Nutcracker) Ballet** | | |
| Selection . . . . . . TSCHAIKOWSKY | V— | 6 |
| **Caucasian Sketches** | | |
| March of the Sardar . . . . IPPOLITOW-IWANOW | V— | 30 |
| **Cavalleria Rusticana** | | |
| Selection . . . . . . MASCAGNI | IV— | 58 |
| *Siciliana* . . . . . . MASCAGNI | VII— | 22 |
| Cavatina, Op. 85, No. 3 . . . . RAFF | II— | 166 |
| **Chabrier, E.** | | |
| Habañera . . . . . . CHABRIER | III— | 194 |
| **Chaminade, C.** | | |
| Flatt'rer, The (La Lisonjera) . . CHAMINADE | III— | 214 |
| Scarf Dance . . . . . . CHAMINADE | III— | 22 |
| Chanson Triste, Op. 40, No. 2 . . TSCHAIKOWSKY | III— | 250 |
| Chant Sans Paroles, Op. 2, No. 3 . TSCHAIKOWSKY | II— | 232 |
| *Children's Hosanna* . . . . WEBB | VII— | 238 |
| **Chimes of Normandy, The** | | |
| Selection . . . . . . PLANQUETTE | V— | 142 |
| Choclo, El (Tango) . . . . . VILLOLDO, A. G. | VI— | 254 |
| **Chopin, Fr.** | | |
| Funeral March, Op. 35, No. 4 . . CHOPIN | VII— | 100 |
| Mazurka, Op. 7, No. 1 . . . CHOPIN | I— | 158 |
| "Minute" Waltz, Op. 64, No. 1 . CHOPIN | I— | 149 |
| Nocturne, Op. 9, No. 2 . . . CHOPIN | I— | 137 |
| Nocturne, Op. 55, No. 1 . . . CHOPIN | I— | 140 |
| Polonaise in A (Military), Op. 40, No. 1 CHOPIN | IX— | 21 |
| Prelude, Op. 28, No. 4 . . . CHOPIN | I— | 152 |
| Prelude, Op. 28, No. 5 . . . CHOPIN | I— | 153 |
| Prelude, Op. 28, No. 6 . . . CHOPIN | I— | 154 |
| Prelude, Op. 28, No. 7 . . . CHOPIN | I— | 155 |
| Prelude, Op. 28, No. 23 . . . CHOPIN | I— | 156 |
| Waltz in A Minor, Op. 34, No. 2 . CHOPIN | I— | 144 |
| *Church's One Foundation, The* . . WESLEY | VII— | 239 |
| **Cid, Le** | | |
| Selection . . . . . . MASSENET | IV— | 64 |
| Cinquantaine, La . . . . . GABRIEL-MARIE | III— | 102 |
| Ciribiribin (Waltz) . . . . . PESTALOZZA | VI— | 124 |

| | VOL. | PAGE |
|---|---|---|
| **Classic Piano Compositions.** See Vols. I and IX | | |
| **College Songs.** See Vol. VIII | | |
| *Come Back to Erin* . . . . CLARIBEI | VIII— | 92 |
| *Come, Holy Spirit* . . . . DYKES | VII— | 254 |
| *Come, Thou Almighty King* . . GIARDINI | VII— | 254 |
| *Come, Thou Fount of Ev'ry Blessing* . WYETH | VII— | 251 |
| *Come Where My Love Lies Dreaming* . FOSTER | VIII— | 191 |
| *Come, Ye Disconsolate* . . . . WEBBE | VII— | 243 |
| **Comic Operas.** See Vols. V and VIII | | |
| *Comin' Thro' the Rye* . . . . SCOTCH SONG | VIII— | 89 |
| Concerto No. 1 in B Flat Minor, Op. 23 | | |
| (Selection) . . . . . TSCHAIKOWSKY | IX— | 41 |
| Confidence, Op. 19, No. 4 . . . MENDELSSOHN | I— | 170 |
| Consolation . . . . . . LISZT | I— | 232 |
| Consolation, Op. 30, No. 3 . . . MENDELSSOHN | I— | 172 |
| **Coppelia (Ballet)** | | |
| Doll Waltz . . . . . . DELIBES | V— | 60 |
| Mazurka and Czardas . . . DELIBES | V— | 54 |
| Valse Lente . . . . . . DELIBES | V— | 50 |
| **Coq d'Or, Le** | | |
| Hymn to the Sun . . . . RIMSKY-KORSAKOW | IV— | 72 |
| Coquette, La . . . . . . BOROWSKI | III— | 220 |
| *Cornfield Medley* . . . . . SOUTHERN SONG | VIII— | 184 |
| *Cradle Hymn* . . . . . ROUSSEAU | VII— | 242 |
| *Cradle Song* . . . . . . BRAHMS | VIII— | 21 |
| Cradle Song . . . . . . HAUSER | III— | 168 |
| Cradle Song . . . . . . ILYINSKY, A. | II— | 68 |
| Crescendo . . . . . . LASSON | II— | 76 |
| *Crown Him with Many Crowns* . . BRIDGES | VII— | 242 |
| *Crucifixion* . . . . . . SPIRITUAL | VII— | 191 |
| **Cui, César** | | |
| Orientale, Op. 50, No. 9 . . . CUI | IX— | 56 |
| Cujus Animam (Stabat Mater) . . ROSSINI | IX— | 146 |
| Cumparsita, La (Tango) . . . RODRIGUEZ | IX— | 132 |
| Cygne, Le (The Swan) . . . . SAINT-SAËNS | II— | 172 |
| Czarine, La (Mazurka) . . . . GANNE | III— | 113 |
| **Dance Music.** See Vols. VI and IX | | |
| Dancing Doll . . . . . . POLDINI | III— | 14 |
| *Darling Nelly Gray* . . . . HANBY | VIII— | 114 |
| *Dat Ol'-Time Religion* . . . . SPIRITUAL | VII— | 203 |
| **Daughter of the Regiment, The** | | |
| Selection . . . . . . DONIZETTI | V— | 118 |
| *Dear Evelina, Sweet Evelina* . . . COLLEGE SONG | VIII— | 217 |
| **Debussy, Claude** | | |
| Prelude to the Afternoon of a Faun | | |
| (Selection) . . . . . DEBUSSY | IX— | 76 |
| Rêverie . . . . . . . DEBUSSY | II— | 34 |
| *Deep in the Heart of Texas* . . . SWANDER | IX— | 226 |
| *Deep River* . . . . . . SPIRITUAL | VII— | 190 |
| **Delibes, L.** | | |
| Coppelia (Doll Waltz) . . . DELIBES | V— | 60 |
| Coppelia (Mazurka and Czardas) . DELIBES | V— | 54 |
| Coppelia (Valse Lente) . . . DELIBES | V— | 50 |
| Naila (Valse Lente) . . . . DELIBES | V— | 64 |
| Passepied . . . . . . DELIBES | III— | 186 |
| Sylvia (Barcarolle and Valse Lente) . DELIBES | V— | 73 |
| Sylvia (Pizzicato) . . . . DELIBES | V— | 78 |
| Dengozo (Maxixe-Tango) . . . NAZARETH | VI— | 240 |
| *Deutscher Tanz (German Dance)* . DITTERSDORF | I— | 58 |
| *Didn't My Lord Deliver Daniel?* . . SPIRITUAL | VII— | 200 |
| **Dittersdorf, C. von** | | |
| German Dance . . . . . DITTERSDORF | I— | 58 |
| *Dixie Land* . . . . . . EMMET | VIII— | 195 |
| Doll, The (Waltzes) . . . . BAYER | VI— | 114 |
| Dolores (Waltzes) . . . . . WALDTEUFEL | VI— | 72 |
| **Donizetti, G.** | | |
| Daughter of the Regiment (Selection) DONIZETTI | V— | 118 |
| Furtive Tear, A (Elixir of Love) . DONIZETTI | VII— | 25 |
| Lucia di Lammermoor (Selection) . DONIZETTI | IV— | 117 |
| *Sextette (Lucia di Lammermoor)* . DONIZETTI | VII— | 48 |
| *Do They Think of Me at Home?* . . GLOVER | VIII— | 146 |
| *Dream of Love (Liebesträum)* . . LISZT, F. | I— | 234 |
| *Dream of Paradise, A* . . . . GRAY | VII— | 150 |
| **Drigo, Richard** | | |
| Pizzicato (Air de Ballet) . . . DRIGO | III— | 66 |
| Serenade (Les Millions d'Arlequin) . DRIGO | III— | 61 |
| Valse Bluette . . . . . DRIGO | III— | 68 |
| *Drink to Me Only with Thine Eyes* . OLD ENGLISH | VIII— | 74 |
| **Duke, Vernon** | | |
| Brooklyn Barcarolle . . . . DUKE | IX— | 118 |

| | | VOL. PAGE |
|---|---|---|
| **Dvořák, Ant.** | | |
| Humoreske, Op. 101, No. 7 | DVOŘÁK | II— 22 |
| Largo (New World Symphony) | DVOŘÁK | II— 30 |
| Slavonic Dance, Op. 46, No. 1 | DVOŘÁK | II— 17 |
| *Songs My Mother Taught Me* | DVOŘÁK | VIII— 60 |
| Waltzes, Op. 54, No. 1 | DVOŘÁK | II— 26 |
| Ecossaisen (Scotch Dances) | BEETHOVEN, L. VAN | I— 34 |
| Egyptian Ballet | LUIGINI | V— 45 |
| Élégie | MASSENET | III— 20 |
| Élégie, Op. 1, No. 3 | YOÚFEROFF | II—254 |
| *Elegy* | MASSENET | VIII— 16 |
| **Elgar, Edward** | | |
| Salut d'Amour | ELGAR | III— 6 |
| Entr'acte Gavotte | GILLET | III -142 |
| Entr'acte (Rosamunde) | SCHUBERT | I—107 |
| Entry of the Gladiators (March) | FUCÍK | VI—225 |
| **Erminie** | | |
| *Lullaby* | JAKOBOWSKI | VIII—140 |
| Selection | JAKOBOWSKI | V—151 |
| Erotik, Op. 43, No. 5 | GRIEG | II— 54 |
| España (Waltzes) | WALDTEUFEL | VI— 60 |
| Estudiantina (Waltzes) | WALDTEUFEL | VI— 85 |
| *Eternal Father, Strong to Save* | DYKES | IX—180 |
| Eugene Onégin | TSCHAIKOWSKY | IV— 84 |
| Evening Hymn | HATTON | VII—217 |
| Evening Prayer (Hansel and Gretel) | HUMPERDINCK | VII— 46 |
| Evening Star (Tannhäuser) | WAGNER | VII— 63 |
| *Ev'ry Time I Feel the Spirit* | SPIRITUAL | VII—192 |
| Extase, L' (Reverie) | GANNE | III -116 |
| Extase, L' (Entr'acte) | THOMÉ | III—238 |
| *Fairest Lord Jesus* | WILLIS | VII—249 |
| **Falla, Manuel de** | | |
| Valse Caprice | FALLA | III— 88 |
| Fantasie No. 3, in D Minor | MOZART | IX— 9 |
| **Fatinitza** | | |
| Selection | SUPPÉ | V—128 |
| **Fauré, Gabriel** | | |
| Romance Sans Paroles, Op. 17, No. 3 | FAURÉ | II— 39 |
| **Faure, J. B.** | | |
| Palm Branches | FAURE | VII— 98 |
| Palms, The | FAURE | VII—179 |
| **Faust** | | |
| Ballet Music | GOUNOD | V— 20 |
| Selection | GOUNOD | IV— 77 |
| Feria, La (Spanish Suite) | LACOME | V— 38 |
| **Fibich, Z.** | | |
| Poéme, Op. 41 | FIBICH | III— 96 |
| Valse Lento, Op. 47 | FIBICH | III— 97 |
| *Fiddle and I* | GOODEVE | VIII— 50 |
| First Heart Throbs (Gavotte) | EILENBERG | III— 83 |
| **Field, John** | | |
| Nocturne in B♭ | FIELD | I—135 |
| **Firebird, The** | | |
| Selection | STRAVINSKY | IX— 81 |
| *Flag of the Free* | WAGNER | VIII—163 |
| *Flatt'rer, The (La Lisonjera)* | CHAMINADE | III—214 |
| **Fledermaus, Die (The Bat)** | | |
| Selection | STRAUSS | V—156 |
| Flirtation (Waltzes) | STECK | VI—128 |
| *Florian's Song* | GODARD | VIII— 44 |
| **Flotow, Fr.** | | |
| *Ah! So Pure (Martha)* | FLOTOW | VII— 54 |
| *Last Rose of Summer, The (Martha)* | FLOTOW | VII— 58 |
| Martha (Selection) | FLOTOW | IV—136 |
| *Flowers That Bloom in the Spring, The (Mikado)* | SULLIVAN, A. S. | VIII—135 |
| *Flow Gently, Sweet Afton* | WELSH SONG | VIII— 88 |
| **Flying Dutchman, The** | | |
| Selection | WAGNER | IV—152 |
| *Forever and a Day* | HADLEY | IX—200 |
| Forget-Me-Not (Intermezzo) | MACBETH | III—212 |
| *Forsaken* | KOSCHAT | VIII—218 |
| *Forty-nine Bottles* | COLLEGE SONG | VIII—215 |
| **Forza del Destino, La** | | |
| Selection | VERDI | IV—112 |
| **Foster, S. C.** | | |
| *Beautiful Dreamer* | FOSTER | VIII—204 |
| *Camptown Races* | FOSTER | VIII—197 |
| *Come Where My Love Lies Dreaming* | FOSTER | VIII—191 |

| | | VOL. PAGE |
|---|---|---|
| *Glendy Burke, The* | FOSTER | VIII—208 |
| *Hard Times Come Again No More* | FOSTER | VIII—198 |
| *Jeanie with the Light Brown Hair* | FOSTER | VIII—209 |
| *Massa's in de Cold Ground* | FOSTER | VIII—199 |
| *My Old Kentucky Home* | FOSTER | VIII—194 |
| *Nelly Bly* | FOSTER | VIII—210 |
| *Nelly Was a Lady* | FOSTER | VIII—206 |
| *Oh! Boys, Carry Me 'Long* | FOSTER | VIII—207 |
| *Oh! Susanna* | FOSTER | VIII—201 |
| *Old Black Joe* | FOSTER | VIII—202 |
| *Old Dog Tray* | FOSTER | VIII—203 |
| *Old Folks at Home, The* | FOSTER | VIII—149 |
| *Ring, Ring de Banjo* | FOSTER | VIII—200 |
| *Uncle Ned* | FOSTER | VIII—179 |
| *Under the Willow She's Sleeping* | FOSTER | VIII—205 |
| **Fra Diavolo** | | |
| Selection | AUBER | V— 93 |
| **Franck, César** | | |
| *Panis Angelicus (Messe Solennelle)* | FRANCK | IX—168 |
| **Freischütz, Der** | | |
| Selection | WEBER | IV— 68 |
| From an Indian Lodge (Woodland Sketches), Op. 51, No. 5 | MACDOWELL | IX— 62 |
| *From Greenland's Icy Mountains* | MASON | VII—244 |
| Funeral March (Sonata, Op. 35) | CHOPIN | VII—100 |
| Funeral March of a Marionette | GOUNOD | III—158 |
| *Funiculi, Funicula* | DENZA | VIII—216 |
| *Für Elise (Album Leaf)* | BEETHOVEN | I— 27 |
| *Furtive Tear, A (Elixir of Love)* | DONIZETTI | VII— 25 |
| *Future Mrs. 'Awkins, The* | CHEVALIER | VIII—113 |
| **Gade, N. W.** | | |
| Spring Flowers | GADE | III— 93 |
| **Ganne, L.** | | |
| Czarine, La (Mazurka) | GANNE | III—112 |
| Extase (Reverie) | GANNE | III—116 |
| Lorraine (Two-Step) | GANNE | VI—236 |
| Gaucho (Tango) | GONZAGA | VI—244 |
| Gavotte (Sixth Violin Sonata) | BACH | I— 12 |
| Gavotte (Iphigenie) | GLUCK | I— 48 |
| Gavotte in D | GOSSEC | I— 56 |
| Gavotte in F | MARTINI | I— 84 |
| German Dance | DITTERSDORF, K. VON | I— 58 |
| **German, Edward** | | |
| Morris Dance (Henry VIII) | GERMAN | III—122 |
| Shepherd's Dance (Henry VIII) | GERMAN | III—125 |
| Torchlight Dance (Henry VIII) | GERMAN | III—129 |
| **Gioconda, La** | | |
| Selection | PONCHIELLI | IV—100 |
| **Gipsy Baron, The** | | |
| Selection | STRAUSS | V—166 |
| Gipsy Rondo | HAYDN | I— 64 |
| *Girl I Left Behind Me, The* | LOVER | VIII—123 |
| **Giroflé-Girofla** | | |
| Selection | LECOCQ | V—114 |
| Gitana, La (Waltzes) | BUCALOSSI | VI—118 |
| **Glazounov, A.** | | |
| Raymonda (Selection) | GLAZOUNOV | V— 82 |
| *Glendy Burke, The* | FOSTER | VIII—208 |
| **Glinka, Michail** | | |
| Russlan and Ludmilla (Selection) | GLINKA | IX— 86 |
| *Glorious Things of Thee Are Spoken* | HAYDN | VII—241 |
| **Gluck, C. W. von** | | |
| Andante (Orfeo) | GLUCK | I— 47 |
| Bourrée (Armide) | GLUCK | I— 51 |
| Caprice (Alceste) | GLUCK | I— 54 |
| Gavotte (Iphigenie) | GLUCK | I— 48 |
| Orfeo (Selection) | GLUCK | IV— 90 |
| **Godard, Benj.** | | |
| Berceuse (Jocelyn) | GODARD | III—156 |
| *Florian's Song* | GODARD | VIII— 44 |
| *Lullaby (Jocelyn)* | GODARD | VII— 76 |
| Mazurka, Op. 54, No. 2 | GODARD | III—178 |
| *God Is Love* | CONKEY | VII—250 |
| *Go Down, Moses* | SPIRITUAL | VII—209 |
| Gold and Silver (Waltzes) | LEHAR | VI—132 |
| **Goldmark, Karl** | | |
| Queen of Sheba, The (Selection) | GOLDMARK | IV—184 |
| Gondellied, Op. 63, No. 3 | SCHARWENKA | II—182 |

| | | | VOL. PAGE |
|---|---|---|---|
| **Gondoliers, The** | | | |
| Selection | . . . . . . . | SULLIVAN . . . . | V—250 |
| Gondolier (Waltzes) | | ROEDER . . . . | VI—136 |
| Good-Bye | . . . . . . . | TOSTI . . . . | VIII— 25 |
| Good-Bye, My Lover, Good-Bye | | COLLEGE SONG . . | VIII—220 |
| Good Night! Good Night, Beloved! (Serenade) | | NEVIN . . . . | IX—208 |
| Good-Night, Ladies | . . . . . | COLLEGE SONG . . | VIII—228 |
| Gopak (Hopak) | . . . . . | MOUSSORGSKY . . | II—124 |
| Gospel Train, De | . . . . . | SPIRITUAL . . . | VII—194 |
| Go to Sleep, Lena Darling | . . | EMMET . . . . | VIII—218 |
| **Gottschalk, L. M.** | | | |
| Berceuse | . . . . . . . | GOTTSCHALK . . | IX— 30 |
| **Gounod, Ch.** | | | |
| Ave Maria | . . . . . . | GOUNOD . . . . | VII—128 |
| Ave Maria | . . . . . . | GOUNOD . . . . | VII—134 |
| Faust | . . . . . . . | GOUNOD . . . . | IV— 77 |
| Faust (Ballet Music) | . . . | GOUNOD . . . . | V— 20 |
| Funeral March of a Marionette | . . | GOUNOD . . . . | III—158 |
| Lovely Flowers, I Pray (Faust) | . | GOUNOD . . . . | VII— 34 |
| Romeo and Juliet | . . . . | GOUNOD . . . . | IV—194 |
| Slumber Song | . . . . . | GOUNOD . . . . | III—162 |
| There Is a Green Hill Far Away | . | GOUNOD . . . . | VII—184 |
| **Granados, E.** | | | |
| Playera, Op. 5, No. 5 | . . . . | GRANADOS . . . | II— 42 |
| **Grand Duchess, The** | | | |
| Selection | . . . . . . . | OFFENBACH . . . | V—180 |
| Grandfather's Clock | . . . . . | WORK . . . . | VIII—153 |
| **Grand Operas, Piano Selections.** See Vols. IV and IX | | | |
| **Grand Operas, Songs from.** See Vol. VII | | | |
| **Grieg, Ed.** | | | |
| Anitra's Dance (Peer Gynt) | . . | GRIEG . . . . | II— 47 |
| An den Frühling, Op. 43, No. 6 | . . | GRIEG . . . . | II— 50 |
| Ase's Death (Peer Gynt) | . . . | GRIEG . . . . | II— 64 |
| Erotik, Op. 43, No. 5 | . . . | GRIEG . . . . | II— 54 |
| I Love Thee (Ich Liebe Dich) | . . | GRIEG . . . . | VIII— 22 |
| Norwegian Dance, Op. 35, No. 2 | . | GRIEG . . . . | II— 56 |
| Norwegian Dance, Op. 35, No. 3 | . | GRIEG . . . . | II— 58 |
| Puck (Kobold), Op. 71, No. 3 | . . | GRIEG . . . . | II— 60 |
| Spring Dance, Op. 38, No. 5 | . . | GRIEG . . . . | II— 67 |
| Grow Old Along with Me | . . . | MANA-ZUCCA . . | IX—212 |
| Habañera (Carmen) | . . . . | BIZET . . . . | VII— 13 |
| Habañera | . . . . . . | CHABRIER . . . | III—194 |
| **Hadley, Henry K.** | | | |
| Forever and a Day | . . . | HADLEY . . . . | IX—200 |
| Hail, Columbia | . . . . . | PHILE . . . . | VIII—160 |
| Hallelujah Chorus (Messiah) | . . | HANDEL . . . . | VII—116 |
| **Handel, G. Fr.** | | | |
| Bourrée in G | . . . . . | HANDEL . . . . | I— 60 |
| Hallelujah Chorus (Messiah) | . . | HANDEL . . . . | VII—116 |
| Largo (Xerxes) | . . . . . | HANDEL . . . . | VII— 87 |
| Sarabande in F | . . . . . | HANDEL . . . . | I— 62 |
| Handful of Keys | . . . . . | WALLER . . . . | IX—125 |
| **Hansel and Gretel** | | | |
| Evening Prayer | . . . . . | HUMPERDINCK . . | VII— 46 |
| Selection | . . . . . | HUMPERDINCK . . | IV—106 |
| Hard Times Come Again No More | . | FOSTER . . . . | VIII—198 |
| Hark! Hark! My Soul | . . . . | DYKES . . . . | VII—211 |
| Hark! Hark! the Lark | . . . . | SCHUBERT . . . | I—116 |
| Hark! Hark! the Lark | . . . . | SCHUBERT . . . | VIII— 12 |
| Hark! the Herald Angels Sing | . . | MENDELSSOHN . . | VII—240 |
| **Harris, Chas. K.** | | | |
| After the Ball | . . . . . | HARRIS . . . . | IX—219 |
| **Hassler, Hans Leo** | | | |
| O Sacred Head (Salve Caput Cruentatum) | HASSLER . . . | IX—175 |
| Haven of Happiness (Valse Lente) | . . | STEGER . . . . | VI—199 |
| **Haydn, Joseph** | | | |
| Andante ("Surprise" Symphony) | . | HAYDN . . . . | I— 76 |
| Gipsy Rondo | . . . . . | HAYDN . . . . | I— 64 |
| Minuet (Symphony in D) | . . | HAYDN . . . . | I— 74 |
| Serenade | . . . . . . | HAYDN . . . . | I— 71 |
| Heaven! and Ocean! (La Gioconda) | . | PONCHIELLI . . | VII— 37 |
| Heav'n Is My Home | . . . | SULLIVAN . . . | VII—238 |
| Heav'nly Aïda (Aïda) | . . . . | VERDI . . . . | VII— 10 |
| **Herbert, Victor** | | | |
| Serenata, La., Op. 3 | . . . . | HERBERT . . . | IX—115 |
| **Herold, Fr.** | | | |
| Zampa (Selection) | . . . . | HEROLD . . . . | IV— 53 |
| He's the Lily of the Valley | . . . | SPIRITUAL . . . | VII—206 |

| | | | VOL. PAGE |
|---|---|---|---|
| Holy God, We Praise Thy Name | . . . | TRADITIONAL . . . | IX—177 |
| Holy, Holy, Holy | . . . . . | DYKES . . . . | VII—237 |
| Holy Night! Peaceful Night! | . . . | GRUBER . . . | VII—232 |
| Home on the Range (Cowboy Song) | . . | TRADITIONAL . . . | IX—222 |
| Home, Sweet Home | . . . . | BISHOP . . . . | VIII—144 |
| **Home Songs.** See Vols. VIII and IX | | | |
| Home to Our Mountains (Il Trovatore) | . | VERDI . . . | VII— 83 |
| Homeward Bound | . . . . . | HARRINGTON . . | VII—252 |
| Hosanna | . . . . . . . | GRANIER . . . | VII—156 |
| **Howard, J. T.** | | | |
| Still Waters | . . . . . . | HOWARD . . . | IX—152 |
| How Can I Leave Thee! | . . . . | FOLK SONG . . . | VIII— 74 |
| How Firm a Foundation | . . . | KEENE . . . . | VII—236 |
| How Gentle God's Commands | . . . | NAEGELI . . . | VII—247 |
| **Huguenots, The** | | | |
| Selection | . . . . . . . | MEYERBEER . . | IV— 95 |
| **Huhn, Bruno** | | | |
| Invictus | . . . . . . . | HUHN . . . . | IX—204 |
| Humoreske, Op. 101, No. 7 | . . . | DVOŘÁK . . . | II— 22 |
| Humoreske, Op. 6 | . . . . . | LEVINE . . . | II— 86 |
| Humoreske, Op. 10, No. 2 | . . . | TSCHAIKOWSKY . . | II—248 |
| **Humorous Songs.** See Vols. VIII and IX | | | |
| **Humperdinck, E.** | | | |
| Evening Prayer (Hansel and Gretel) | . | HUMPERDINCK . . | VII— 46 |
| Hansel and Gretel (Selection) | . . | HUMPERDINCK . . | IV—106 |
| Hungarian Dance, No. 5 | . . . . | BRAHMS . . . | II— 6 |
| Hungarian Rhapsody, No. 2 | . . . | LISZT . . . . | I—240 |
| **Hymns.** See Vols. VII and IX | | | |
| I Am Alone (Manon) | . . . . | MASSENET . . . | VII— 43 |
| I Cannot Sing the Old Songs | . . . | CLARIBEL . . . | VIII—147 |
| I Couldn't Hear Nobody Pray | . . . | SPIRITUAL . . . | VII—193 |
| I Dreamt That I Dwelt in Marble Halls (Bohemian Girl) | | BALFE . . . . | VII— 20 |
| Idyl, Op. 28, No. 1 | . . . . . | MACDOWELL . . | II—105 |
| **If I Were King** | | | |
| Selection | . . . . . . . | ADAM . . . . | V—109 |
| I'll Sing Thee Songs of Araby | . . . | CLAY . . . . | VIII— 73 |
| I Love Thee (Ich Liebe Dich) | . . | GRIEG . . . . | VIII— 22 |
| I'm a Pilgrim | . . . . . | DANA . . . . | VII—233 |
| I'm a-Rolling | . . . . . | SPIRITUAL . . . | VII—199 |
| I'm Called Little Buttercup (Pinafore) | . | SULLIVAN . . . | VIII—138 |
| I Need Thee Ev'ry Hour | . . . | LOWRY . . . . | VII—225 |
| Inflammatus (Stabat Mater) | . . | ROSSINI . . . | VII—108 |
| In Happy Moments Day by Day (Maritana) | | WALLACE . . . | VII— 52 |
| In Heavenly Love Abiding | . . | MENDELSSOHN . . | VII—232 |
| In Old Madrid | . . . . . | TROTERE . . . | VIII— 37 |
| Intermezzo, Op. 117, No. 1 | . . | BRAHMS . . . | II— 14 |
| Intermezzo, Op. 3 | . . . . . | SZALIT . . . | III—236 |
| Intermezzo Russe | . . . . | FRANKE . . . | III— 98 |
| In the Gloaming | . . . . . | HARRISON . . . | VIII— 78 |
| In the Sweet By and By | . . . | WEBSTER . . . | VII—246 |
| Invictus | . . . . . . | HUHN . . . . | IX—204 |
| Invitation to the Dance | . . . | WEBER . . . . | I—160 |
| **Iolanthe** | | | |
| Selection | . . . . . . . | SULLIVAN . . . | V—243 |
| **Ippolitow-Iwanow, I.** | | | |
| Entrance of the Sardar (Caucasian Sketches) | | IPPOLITOW-IWANOW . | V— 30 |
| Irresistible El (Argentine Tango) | . . | LOGATTI . . . | VI—246 |
| I'se Gwine Back to Dixie | . . . | WHITE . . . . | VIII—188 |
| It Came upon the Midnight Clear | . . | WILLIS . . . . | VII—235 |
| It Was Not So to Be (Trumpeter of Sakkingen) | | NESSLER . . . | VIII—124 |
| I Want to See the Old Home | . . . | STEWART . . . | VIII—211 |
| I Would that My Love | . . . | MENDELSSOHN . . | VIII— 70 |
| Jeanie with the Light Brown Hair | . | FOSTER . . . . | VIII—209 |
| Jerusalem | . . . . . . | PARKER . . . . | VII—162 |
| Jerusalem the Golden | . . . | EWING . . . . | VII—231 |
| Jesu, Joy of Man's Desiring | . . | BACH . . . . | IX—157 |
| Jesus Christ Is Ris'n To-day | . . | WORGAN . . . | VII—256 |
| Jesus Lives! | . . . . . | GAUNTLETT . . | VII—224 |
| Jesus, Lover of My Soul | . . . | MARSH . . . . | VII—230 |
| Jesus, My Lord, My God, My All | . | TRADITIONAL . . | IX—176 |
| Jesus! the Very Thought of Thee | . | DYKES . . . . | VII—247 |
| Jingle Bells | . . . . . | COLLEGE SONG . . | VIII—213 |
| Jolly Fellows (Waltzes) | . . . | VOLLSTEDT . . | VI—140 |
| Joy to the World | . . . . | HANDEL . . . | VII—229 |
| Juanita | . . . . . . . | COLLEGE SONG . . | VIII—229 |
| "June" Barcarolle, Op. 37, No. 6 | . . | TSCHAIKOWSKY . . | II—240 |

| | | VOL. PAGE |
|---|---|---|
| *Just As I Am* | BRADBURY | VII—246 |
| Kamennoi-Ostrow, Op. 10, No. 22 | RUBINSTEIN | I—222 |
| *Kathleen Mavourneen* | CROUCH | VIII— 90 |
| *Keep a-Inching Along* | SPIRITUAL | VII—204 |
| *Kerry Dance, The* | MOLLOY | VIII— 94 |
| *Kingdom Coming* | WORK | VIII—186 |
| *Know'st Thou Yonder Land?* (*Mignon*) | THOMAS | VII— 60 |
| Kol Nidrei | HEBREW MELODY | VII—104 |

**Kunihild**

| | | |
|---|---|---|
| Introduction, Act III | KISTLER | IV—254 |
| Largo (New World Symphony) | DVOŘÁK | II— 30 |
| Largo (Xerxes) | HANDEL | VII— 87 |
| *Last Night* | KJERULF | VIII— 79 |
| *Last Rose of Summer, The* (*Martha*) | FLOTOW | VII— 58 |
| *Lazybones* | CARMICHAEL AND MERCER | IX—234 |
| *Lead, Kindly Light* | DYKES | VII—228 |

**Leoncavallo, R.**

| | | |
|---|---|---|
| Selection (Pagliacci) | LEONCAVALLO | IV—161 |
| *Vesti la Giubba* (*Pagliacci*) | LEONCAVALLO | VII— 40 |
| Liebesträum | LISZT | I—234 |

**Light Cavalry**

| | | |
|---|---|---|
| Selection | SUPPÉ | V—132 |

**Light Piano Compositions.** See Vols. III and IX

| | | |
|---|---|---|
| *Listen to the Mocking Bird* | HAWTHORNE | VIII—171 |

**Liszt, Franz**

| | | |
|---|---|---|
| Consolation | LISZT | I—232 |
| Hungarian Rhapsody No. 2 | LISZT | I—240 |
| Liebesträum | LISZT | I—234 |
| *Little Bit of Heaven, A* | BALL | IX—216 |
| *Little Wheel a-Turnin' in My Heart* | SPIRITUAL | VII—195 |

**Lohengrin**

| | | |
|---|---|---|
| Selection | WAGNER | IV—122 |
| *Loin du Bal* | GILLET | III—148 |
| *Londonderry Air* | IRISH FOLK SONG | VIII— 64 |
| *Long, Long Ago* | BAYLY | VIII— 84 |
| *Loreley, The* | SILCHER | VIII— 72 |
| *Lorraine* (Two-Step) | GANNE | VI—236 |
| *Lost Chord, The* | SULLIVAN | VII—168 |
| Loure (Third 'Cello Suite) | BACH | I— 8 |
| *Love Dreams* | BLON | III— 30 |
| *Lovely Flowers, I Pray* (*Faust*) | GOUNOD | VII— 34 |
| *Lovely Night* (*Tales of Hoffman*) | OFFENBACH | VII— 72 |
| *Love's Dream After the Ball* | CZIBULKA | III— 50 |
| *Love's Dreamland* (Waltzes) | ROEDER | VI—144 |
| *Love's Old Sweet Song* | MOLLOY | VIII— 48 |

**Love Songs.** See Vols. VIII and IX

| | | |
|---|---|---|
| *Love's Springtime* | EHRICH | III— 78 |
| *Love's the Tune* (*A Waltz Dream*) | STRAUS | VIII—125 |
| *Love Thoughts* | HAWAIIAN FOLK SONG | VIII—118 |
| *Low Back'd Car, The* | LOVER | VIII— 98 |

**Lucia di Lammermoor**

| | | |
|---|---|---|
| Selection | DONIZETTI | IV—117 |
| *Sextette* | DONIZETTI | VII— 48 |
| Lullaby, A | TEMPLETON | IX—122 |
| *Lullaby* (*Erminie*) | JAKOBOWSKI | VIII—140 |
| *Lullaby* (*Jocelyn*) | GODARD | VII— 76 |

**MacDowell, E.**

| | | |
|---|---|---|
| A.D.MDCXX (Sea Pieces), Op. 55, No. 3 | MACDOWELL | IX— 59 |
| From an Indian Lodge (Woodland Sketches), Op. 51, No. 5 | MACDOWELL | IX— 62 |
| Idyl, Op. 28, No. 1 | MACDOWELL | II—105 |
| Scotch Poem, Op. 31, No. 2 | MACDOWELL | II—108 |
| Witches' Dance, Op. 17, No. 2 | MACDOWELL | II— 96 |

**MacGimsey, Robert**

| | | |
|---|---|---|
| *Abraham* | MACGIMSEY | IX—194 |

**Magic Flute, The**

| | | |
|---|---|---|
| Selection | MOZART | IV— 42 |

**Mana-Zucca**

| | | |
|---|---|---|
| *Grow Old Along with Me* | MANA-ZUCCA | IX—212 |

**Manon**

| | | |
|---|---|---|
| Selection | MASSENET | IV—128 |
| Marche Militaire, Op. 51, No. 1 | SCHUBERT | I—113 |
| *March of the Little Pierrots* | BOSC | VI—228 |
| *Marcheta* | SCHERTZINGER | IX—214 |
| *Maria, Mari!* | CAPUA | VIII—104 |
| *Marie, Mine* | HUNGARIAN SONG | VIII—102 |
| *Marine's Hymn, The* | TRADITIONAL | IX—240 |

**Maritana**

| | | |
|---|---|---|
| Selection | WALLACE | IV—132 |

**Martha**

| | | |
|---|---|---|
| *Ah! So Pure* | FLOTOW | VII— 54 |
| Selection | FLOTOW | IV—136 |
| *Maryland! My Maryland!* | RANDALL | VIII—182 |

**Mascagni, P.**

| | | |
|---|---|---|
| *Ave Maria* (*Cavalleria Rusticana*) | MASCAGNI | VII—144 |
| Selection (*Cavalleria Rusticana*) | MASCAGNI | IV— 58 |
| *Siciliana* (*Cavalleria Rusticana*) | MASCAGNI | VII— 22 |

**Mascot, The**

| | | |
|---|---|---|
| Selection | AUDRAN | V— 98 |
| *Massa's in de Cold Ground* | FOSTER | VIII—199 |

**Massenet, J.**

| | | |
|---|---|---|
| Angelus, The | MASSENET | VII—122 |
| Cid, Le | MASSENET | IV— 64 |
| Élégie | MASSENET | III— 20 |
| *Elegy* | MASSENET | VIII— 16 |
| *I Am Alone* (*Manon*) | MASSENET | VII— 43 |
| Manon | MASSENET | IV—128 |
| *Prayer* (*Le Cid*) | MASSENET | VII— 28 |

**Mastersingers of Nurnberg, The**

| | | |
|---|---|---|
| Selection | WAGNER | IV—141 |
| Mazurka, Op. 7, No. 1 | CHOPIN | I—158 |
| *May Night* | PALMGREN | II—139 |
| Mazurka, Op. 54, No. 2 | GODARD | III—178 |
| Mazurka, Op. 40, No. 2 | MEYER-HELMUND | III—199 |

**Mefistofele**

| | | |
|---|---|---|
| Selection | BOITO | IV—157 |
| Mèlodie, Op. 18, No. 1 | MOSZKOWSKI | II—115 |
| Mèlodie, Op. 8, No. 3 | PADEREWSKI | II—136 |
| Mèlodie, Op. 1 | STOJOWSKI | III—234 |
| Mèlodie, Op. 42, No. 3 | TSCHAIKOWSKY | II—244 |
| Melody in F, Op. 3, No. 1 | RUBINSTEIN | I—216 |

**Mendelssohn, Felix**

| | | |
|---|---|---|
| Confidence, Op. 19, No. 4 | MENDELSSOHN | I—170 |
| Consolation, Op. 30, No. 3 | MENDELSSOHN | I—172 |
| *Hark! the Herald Angels Sing* | MENDELSSOHN | VII—240 |
| *I Would That My Love* | MENDELSSOHN | VIII— 70 |
| *O, Rest in the Lord* (*Elijah*) | MENDELSSOHN | VII—131 |
| Rondo Capriccioso, Op. 14 | MENDELSSOHN | I—182 |
| Spinning Song, Op. 67, No. 4 | MENDELSSOHN | I—173 |
| Spring Song, Op. 62, No. 6 | MENDELSSOHN | I—178 |
| Wedding March | MENDELSSOHN | I—193 |
| Menuet à l'antique | PADEREWSKI | II—130 |

**Merry Widow, The**

| | | |
|---|---|---|
| Selection | LEHAR | V—192 |
| *Vilia Song* | LEHAR | VIII—130 |
| *Waltz Song* | LEHAR | VIII—132 |
| Waltzes | LEHAR | VI—187 |

**Merry Wives of Windsor, The**

| | | |
|---|---|---|
| Overture | NICOLAI | V— 86 |

**Meyerbeer, G.**

| | | |
|---|---|---|
| Huguenots, The (Selection) | MEYERBEER | IV— 95 |
| Prophète, Le (Selection) | MEYERBEER | IV— 46 |
| *Mighty Fortress Is Our God, A* | LUTHER | VII—227 |

**Mignon**

| | | |
|---|---|---|
| *Know'st Thou Yonder Land?* | THOMAS | VII— 60 |
| Selection | THOMAS | IV—146 |

**Mikado, The**

| | | |
|---|---|---|
| *Flowers That Bloom in the Spring* | SULLIVAN | VIII—135 |
| Selection | SULLIVAN | V—236 |

**Minstrel Songs.** See Vols. VIII and IX

| | | |
|---|---|---|
| Minuet (Symphony in D) | HAYDN | I— 74 |
| Minuet (Divertimento, No. 1) | MOZART | I—132 |
| Minuet (Don Juan) | MOZART | I—122 |
| Minuet (Sonata, Op. 78) | SCHUBERT | I—104 |
| Minuet in A | BOCCHERINI | I— 88 |
| Minuet in G | BEETHOVEN | I— 24 |
| Minuet, Op. 56 | SAINT-SAËNS | II—176 |
| Minuets (Second Partitur) | BACH | I— 10 |
| "Minute" Waltz, Op. 64, No. 1 | CHOPIN | I—149 |
| *Mistah Shakespeah* | CADMAN | IX—196 |

**Modern Piano Compositions.** See Vols. VII and IX

| | | |
|---|---|---|
| *Mona* | ADAMS | VIII— 56 |
| Moment Musical, Op. 94, No. 3 | SCHUBERT | I—102 |
| Monte Cristo (Waltzes) | KOTLAR | VI—148 |
| Morning Journals (Waltzes) | STRAUSS | VI— 11 |
| Morris Dance (Henry VIII) | GERMAN | III—122 |
| Moss Rose (Valse Lente) | BOSC | VI—204 |

| | | VOL. PAGE |
|---|---|---|
| **Moszkowski, M.** | | |
| Melodie, Op. 18, No. 1 | MOSZKOWSKI | II—115 |
| Serenata, Op. 15, No. 1 | MOSZKOWSKI | II—118 |
| Spanish Dance, Op. 12, No. 1 | MOSZKOWSKI | II—112 |
| Spanish Dance, Op. 12, No. 2 | MOSZKOWSKI | II—120 |
| **Moussorgsky, M.** | | |
| Boris Godounov (Selection) | MOUSSORGSKY | IV— 22 |
| Gopak (Hopak) | MOUSSORGSKY | II—124 |
| Tear, A (Un Larme) | MOUSSORGSKY | III—218 |
| Mozart Matriculates | TEMPLETON | IX—120 |
| **Mozart, W. A.** | | |
| Fantasie No. 3, in D Minor | MOZART | IX— 9 |
| Magic Flute (Selection) | MOZART | IV— 42 |
| Minuet (Divertimento No. 1) | MOZART | I—132 |
| Minuet (Don Juan) | MOZART | I—122 |
| Sonata in C (First Movement) | MOZART | I—128 |
| Turkish March (Sonata in A) | MOZART | I—124 |
| Murmuring Zephyrs | JENSEN | II— 70 |
| Music Box, A, Op. 32 | LIADOW | II— 91 |
| My Bonnie | COLLEGE SONG | VIII—230 |
| My Dream (Waltzes) | WALDTEUFEL | VI— 80 |
| My Faith Looks Up to Thee | MASON | VII—240 |
| My Heart at Thy Sweet Voice (Samson and Delilah) | SAINT-SAËNS | VII— 68 |
| My Old Dutch | INGLE | VIII—111 |
| My Old Kentucky Home | FOSTER | VIII—194 |
| My Treasure (Waltzes) | BECUCCI | VI—182 |
| Nachtstück, Op. 23, No. 4 | SCHUMANN | I—199 |
| Naila (Valse Lente) | DELIBES | V— 64 |
| Nearer, My God, To Thee | MASON | VII—221 |
| **Negro Spirituals.** See Vol. VII | | |
| Nelly Bly | FOSTER | VIII—210 |
| Nelly Was a Lady | FOSTER | VIII—206 |
| **Nevin, E. W.** | | |
| Serenade (Good Night! Good Night, Beloved!) | NEVIN | IX—208 |
| New Vienna (Waltzes) | STRAUSS | VI— 36 |
| **Nicolai, Otto** | | |
| Merry Wives of Windsor, The (Overture) | NICOLAI | V— 86 |
| Night Frolic (Valse Lente) | SPACEK | VI—219 |
| Ninety and Nine, The | SANKEY | VII—226 |
| Nobody Knows de Trouble I've Seen | SPIRITUAL | VII—197 |
| Nocturne (Petite Suite) | BORODIN | IX— 48 |
| Nocturne, Op. 9, No. 2 | CHOPIN | I—137 |
| Nocturne, Op. 55, No. 1 | CHOPIN | I—140 |
| Nocturne in Bb | FIELD | I—135 |
| Nocturne, Op. 9, No. 2 | SCRIABIN | IX— 52 |
| Non é Ver ('Tis Not True) | MATTEI | VIII— 34 |
| **Norma** | | |
| Selection | BELLINI | IV— 31 |
| Norwegian Dance, Op. 35, No. 2 | GRIEG | II— 56 |
| Norwegian Dance, Op. 35, No. 3 | GRIEG | II— 58 |
| No Shadows Yonder (Holy City) | GAUL | VII—176 |
| Now the Day Is Over | BARNBY | VIII—236 |
| Nut Brown Maiden | COLLEGE SONG | VIII—231 |
| **Nutcracker (Casse-Noisette) Suite** | | |
| Selection | TSCHAIKOWSKY | V— 6 |
| **Oberon** | | |
| Selection | WEBER | IV—204 |
| O Blodwen, My True Love | PARRY | VIII— 86 |
| Obstination | FONTENAILLES | VIII— 46 |
| O Come, All Ye Faithful | READING | VII—253 |
| **Offenbach, J.** | | |
| Grand Duchess, The (Selection) | OFFENBACH | V—180 |
| Lovely Night (Tales of Hoffman) | OFFENBACH | VII— 72 |
| Orpheus in the Underworld | OFFENBACH | V—172 |
| Tales of Hoffman, The | OFFENBACH | V—184 |
| O God, Our Help in Ages Past | CROFT | VII—230 |
| Oh! Boys, Carry Me 'Long | FOSTER | VIII—207 |
| Oh! dem Golden Slippers! | BLAND | VIII—178 |
| Oh, Happy Day! | DODDRIDGE | VII—220 |
| Oh, My Darling Clementine | MONTROSE | VIII—222 |
| Oh! Susanna | FOSTER | VIII—201 |
| O Jesus, Thou Art Standing | KNECHT | VII—224 |
| Ol' Darkie, Ol' Mule | WARING | IX—191 |
| Old Black Joe | FOSTER | VIII—202 |
| Old Cabin Home, The | SOUTHERN SONG | VIII—177 |
| Old Dog Tray | FOSTER | VIII—203 |
| Old Folks at Home, The | FOSTER | VIII—149 |
| Old Hundred | BOURGEOIS | VII—228 |
| Old Oaken Bucket, The | KIALLMARK | VIII—148 |
| Old Rugged Cross, The | BENNARD | IX—181 |

| | | VOL. PAGE |
|---|---|---|
| **Olivette** | | |
| Selection | AUDRAN | V—104 |
| One Heart, One Mind (Polka Mazurka) | STRAUSS | VI— 56 |
| One Sweetly Solemn Thought | AMBROSE | VII—172 |
| One Sweetly Solemn Thought | WEBER | VII—215 |
| Only the Sad of Heart | TSCHAIKOWSKY | VIII— 18 |
| Onward, Christian Soldiers | SULLIVAN | VII—223 |
| O Paradise! | BARNBY | VII—222 |
| **Operas.** See Vols. IV, V, VII, VIII, and IX | | |
| O, Rest in the Lord (Elijah) | MENDELSSOHN | VII—131 |
| **Orfeo** | | |
| Selection | GLUCK | IV— 90 |
| Orientale, Op. 50, No. 9 | CUI | IX— 56 |
| **Orpheus in the Underworld** | | |
| Selection | OFFENBACH | V—172 |
| O Sacred Head | HASSLER | IX—175 |
| O Sole Mio! | CAPUA | VIII—101 |
| O Thou Joyful Day | SMUCKER | VII—250 |
| Over the Banister | COLLEGE SONG | VIII—223 |
| Over the Stars There Is Rest | ABT | VII—182 |
| Over the Waves (Waltzes) | ROSAS | VI—152 |
| **Paderewski, I.** | | |
| Melodie, Op. 8, No. 3 | PADEREWSKI | II—136 |
| Menuet à l'antique | PADEREWSKI | II—130 |
| **Pagliacci, I.** | | |
| Selection | LEONCAVALLO | IV—161 |
| Vesti la Guibba | LEONCAVALLO | VII— 40 |
| Palm Branches | FAURE | VII— 98 |
| **Palmgren, S.** | | |
| May Night | PALMGREN | II—139 |
| Palms, The | FAURE | VII—179 |
| Paloma, La | YRADIER | III—252 |
| Paloma, La | YRADIER | VIII— 66 |
| Panis Angelicus (Messe Solennelle) | FRANCK | IX—168 |
| Papillon, Le (The Butterfly) | LAVALLÉE | II— 79 |
| **Parsifal** | | |
| Selection | WAGNER | IV—168 |
| Passepied | DELIBES | III—186 |
| Pastorale in E Minor | SCARLATTI | IX— 6 |
| **Patience** | | |
| Selection | SULLIVAN | V—224 |
| **Patriotic Songs (American).** See Vols. VIII and IX | | |
| Pavane | RAVEL | IX— 64 |
| Peter, Go Ring dem Bells | SPIRITUAL | VII—207 |
| **Peter and the Wolf** | | |
| Selection | PROKOFIEFF | IX— 69 |
| **Pierné, Gabriel** | | |
| Serenade | PIERNÉ | II—142 |
| **Pinafore, H. M. S.** | | |
| I'm Called Little Buttercup | SULLIVAN | VIII—138 |
| Selection | SULLIVAN | V—218 |
| **Pirates of Penzance, The** | | |
| Poor Wand'ring One | SULLIVAN | VIII—136 |
| Selection | SULLIVAN | V—210 |
| Pizzicato (Air de Ballet) | DRIGO | III— 66 |
| Pizzicato-Polka | STRAUSS | VI— 58 |
| **Plantation Songs.** See Vols. VIII and IX | | |
| Playera, Op. 5, No. 5 | GRANADOS | II— 42 |
| Pleyel's Hymn | PLEYEL | VII—226 |
| Poéme, Op. 41 | FIBICH | III— 96 |
| **Poet and Peasant** | | |
| Selection | SUPPÉ | V—121 |
| Polichinelle, Op. 3, No. 4 | RACHMANINOFF | II—158 |
| Polish Dance, Op. 3, No. 1 | SCHARWENKA | III—230 |
| Polly-Wolly-Doodle | COLLEGE SONG | VIII—183 |
| Polonaise in A (Military), Op. 40, No. 1 | CHOPIN | IX— 21 |
| **Ponchielli, A.** | | |
| Gioconda, La | PONCHIELLI | IV—100 |
| Heaven! and Ocean! (La Gioconda) | PONCHIELLI | VII— 37 |
| Poor Old Slave, The | SOUTHERN SONG | VIII—174 |
| Poor Wand'ring One (Pirates of Penzance) | SULLIVAN | VIII—136 |
| Poupée Valsante (Dancing Doll) | POLDINI | III— 17 |
| Prayer (Le Cid) | MASSENET | VII— 28 |
| Prayer | WEBER | VII—189 |
| Prelude in C | BACH | I— 6 |
| Prelude, Op. 28, No. 4 | CHOPIN | I—152 |

| | VOL. | PAGE |
|---|---|---|
| Prelude, Op. 28, No. 5 . . . . . CHOPIN . . . . | I— | 153 |
| Prelude, Op. 28, No. 6 . . . . . CHOPIN . . . . | I— | 154 |
| Prelude, Op. 28, No. 7 . . . . . CHOPIN . . . . | I— | 155 |
| Prelude, Op. 28, No. 23 . . . . CHOPIN . . . . | I— | 156 |
| Prelude in C Sharp Minor . . . RACHMANINOFF . . | II— | 147 |
| Prelude, Op. 23, No. 5 . . . . RACHMANINOFF . . | II— | 152 |
| Prelude, Op. 9, No. 1 . . . . SCRIABIN . . . . | IX— | 50 |
| Prelude in E Flat, Op. 34, No. 19 . SHOSTAKOVITCH . . | IX— | 74 |

**Prelude to the Afternoon of a Faun**
| Selection . . . . . . . DEBUSSY . . . . | IX— | 76 |

**Prince Igor**
| Selection . . . . . . . BORODIN . . . . | IV— | 174 |
| Procession of the Sardar (Caucasian Sketches) . . . . . . . IPPOLITOW-IWANOW . | V— | 30 |

**Prokofieff, S.**
| Peter and the Wolf (Selection) . . PROKOFIEFF . . . | IX— | 69 |

**Prophète, Le**
| Selection . . . . . . . MEYERBEER . . . | IV— | 46 |

**Puccini, G.**
| Villi, Le (Selection) . . . . . PUCCINI . . . . | IV— | 189 |
| Puck (Kobold), Op. 71, No. 3 . . . GRIEG . . . . | II— | 60 |

**Queen of Sheba, The**
| Selection . . . . . . . GOLDMARK . . . . | IV— | 184 |

**Queen's Lace Handkerchief, The**
| Selection . . . . . . . STRAUSS . . . . | V— | 160 |
| Quietude . . . . . . . GREGH . . . . | III— | 164 |
| Quilting Party, The . . . . . COLLEGE SONG . . | VIII— | 228 |

**Rachmaninoff, S.**
| Polichinelle, Op. 3, No. 4 . . . RACHMANINOFF . . | II— | 158 |
| Prelude in C Sharp Minor . . . RACHMANINOFF . . | II— | 147 |
| Prelude, Op. 23, No. 5 . . . . RACHMANINOFF . . | II— | 152 |
| Romance . . . . . . . RACHMANINOFF . . | II— | 164 |

**Ravel, Maurice**
| Pavane . . . . . . . RAVEL . . . . | IX— | 64 |

**Raymond**
| Selection . . . . . . . THOMAS . . . . | IV— | 179 |

**Raymonda (Ballet)**
| Selection . . . . . . . GLAZOUNOV . . . | V— | 82 |
| Red, White, and Blue, The . . . BECKET . . . . | VIII— | 162 |
| Rejoice, Ye Pure in Heart . . . MESSITER . . . | IX— | 178 |
| Rest for the Weary . . . . . McDONALD . . . | VII— | 216 |
| Return of Spring (Waltzes) . . . WALDTEUFEL . . | VI— | 104 |
| Rêverie . . . . . . . . DEBUSSY . . . . | II— | 34 |

**Rigoletto**
| Donna è Mobile, La (Woman is Fickle) . VERDI . . . . | VII— | 66 |
| Selection . . . . . . . VERDI . . . . | IV— | 208 |

**Rimsky-Korsakow, M.**
| Coq d'Or, Le . . . . . . RIMSKY-KORSAKOW . | IV— | 72 |
| Romance, Op. 15, No. 2 . . . . RIMSKY-KORSAKOW . | II— | 170 |
| Sadko (Selection) . . . . . RIMSKY-KORSAKOW . | IV— | 228 |
| Sheherazade (Selection) . . . RIMSKY-KORSAKOW . | IV— | 220 |
| Snow-Maiden, The (Selection) . . RIMSKY-KORSAKOW . | IV— | 214 |
| Song of India, A (Sadko) . . . . RIMSKY-KORSAKOW . | VII— | 6 |
| Ring, Ring de Banjo . . . . FOSTER . . . . | VIII— | 200 |
| Robin Adair . . . . . . KEPPEL . . . . | VIII— | 75 |
| Rock'd in the Cradle of the Deep . . KNIGHT . . . . | VII— | 148 |
| Rock of Ages . . . . . . HASTINGS . . . | VII— | 214 |
| Roll, Jordan, Roll . . . . . SPIRITUAL . . . | VII— | 196 |
| Romance . . . . . . . RACHMANINOFF . . | II— | 164 |
| Romance, Op. 85, No. 3 . . . . RAFF . . . . | II— | 166 |
| Romance, Op. 15, No. 2 . . . . RIMSKY-KORSAKOW . | II— | 170 |
| Romance, Op. 44, No. 1 . . . . RUBINSTEIN . . | I— | 230 |
| Romance, Op. 24, No. 9 . . . . SIBELIUS . . . | II— | 194 |
| Romance, Op. 5 . . . . . TSCHAIKOWSKY . . | II— | 235 |
| Romance Sans Paroles, Op. 17, No. 3 . FAURÉ . . . . | II— | 39 |
| Romance in F Sharp, Op. 28, No. 2 . SCHUMANN . . . | IX— | 28 |

**Romantic Piano Compositions.** See Vols. I and IX

**Romeo and Juliet**
| Selection . . . . . . . GOUNOD . . . . | IV— | 194 |
| Romeo and Juliet (Selection) . . TSCHAIKOWSKY . . | IX— | 36 |
| Rondo in C, Op. 51, No. 1 . . . BEETHOVEN . . . | IX— | 14 |
| Rondo Capriccioso, Op. 14 . . . MENDELSSOHN . . | I— | 182 |
| Rosa Lee . . . . . . . SOUTHERN SONG . | VIII— | 187 |
| Roses from the South (Waltzes) . . STRAUSS . . . . | VI— | 16 |

**Rossini, G.**
| Cujus Animam (Stabat Mater) . . ROSSINI . . . . | IX— | 146 |
| Inflammatus (Stabat Mater) . . ROSSINI . . . . | VII— | 108 |
| William Tell (Selection) . . . ROSSINI . . . . | IV— | 231 |

| | VOL. | PAGE |
|---|---|---|

**Rubinstein, Anton**
| Kamennoi-Ostrow, Op. 10, No. 22 . RUBINSTEIN . . . | I— | 222 |
| Melody in F, Op. 3, No. 1 . . . . RUBINSTEIN . . . | I— | 216 |
| Romance, Op. 44, No. 1 . . . . RUBINSTEIN . . . | I— | 230 |
| Toréador et Andalouse . . . . RUBINSTEIN . . . | I— | 213 |

**Ruddygore**
| Selection . . . . . . . SULLIVAN . . . | V— | 229 |

**Russlan and Ludmilla**
| Selection . . . . . . . GLINKA . . . . | IX— | 86 |
| Rustle of Spring, Op. 32, No. 3 . . . SINDING . . . . | II— | 204 |

**Sacred Piano Music.** See Vols. VII and IX

**Sacred Songs.** See Vols. VII and IX

**Sadko**
| Selection . . . . . . . RIMSKY-KORSAKOW . | IV— | 228 |
| Song of India . . . . . . RIMSKY-KORSAKOW . | VII— | 6 |

**Saint-Saens, C.**
| Cygne, Le (The Swan) . . . . SAINT-SAËNS . . . | II— | 73 |
| Minuet, Op. 56 . . . . . . SAINT-SAËNS . . . | II— | 176 |
| My Heart at Thy Sweet Voice (Samson and Delilah) . . . . . . SAINT-SAËNS . . . | VII— | 68 |
| Samson and Delilah (Selection) . SAINT-SAËNS . . . | IV— | 199 |
| Sailing . . . . . . . MARKS . . . . | VIII— | 224 |
| Sally, Come Up . . . . . SOUTHERN SONG . | VIII— | 190 |
| Sally in Our Alley . . . . . CAREY . . . . | VIII— | 83 |
| Salut d'Amour . . . . . . ELGAR . . . . | III— | 6 |

**Samson and Delilah**
| My Heart at Thy Sweet Voice . . SAINT-SAËNS . . . | VII— | 68 |
| Selection . . . . . . . SAINT-SAËNS . . . | IV— | 199 |
| Santa Lucia . . . . . . NEAPOLITAN SONG . | VIII— | 119 |
| Santiago (Spanish Waltzes) . . . CORBIN . . . . | VI— | 156 |
| Sarabande in F . . . . . HANDEL . . . . | I— | 62 |
| Saviour, Again to Thy Dear Name . HOPKINS . . . . | IX— | 179 |
| Scarf Dance . . . . . . CHAMINADE . . . | III— | 22 |

**Scarlatti, D.**
| Pastorale in E Minor . . . . SCARLATTI . . . | IX— | 6 |
| Tempo di Ballo . . . . . SCARLATTI . . . | I— | 80 |
| Schlummerlied . . . . . . SCHUMANN . . . | I— | 202 |

**Schubert, Franz**
| Adagio (Octet, Op. 166) . . . . SCHUBERT . . . | I— | 100 |
| Ave Maria . . . . . . . SCHUBERT . . . | VII— | 126 |
| Ave Maria . . . . . . . SCHUBERT . . . | IX— | 162 |
| Ballet Music (Rosamunde) . . . SCHUBERT . . . | I— | 110 |
| Entr'acte (Rosamunde) . . . . SCHUBERT . . . | I— | 107 |
| Hark! Hark! the Lark . . . . SCHUBERT . . . | I— | 116 |
| Hark! Hark! the Lark . . . . SCHUBERT . . . | VIII— | 12 |
| Marche Militaire, Op. 51, No. 1 . . SCHUBERT . . . | I— | 113 |
| Minuet (Sonata, Op. 78) . . . SCHUBERT . . . | I— | 104 |
| Moment Musical, Op. 94, No. 3 . . SCHUBERT . . . | I— | 102 |
| Serenade (Ständchen) . . . . SCHUBERT . . . | I— | 118 |
| Serenade . . . . . . . SCHUBERT . . . | VIII— | 8 |
| Unfinished Symphony (First Movement) . . . . . . . SCHUBERT . . . | I— | 91 |
| Waltzes (Selected from Op. 9a) . . SCHUBERT . . . | I— | 96 |
| Who Is Sylvia? . . . . . . SCHUBERT . . . | VIII— | 14 |

**Schumann, R.**
| Aufschwung (Soaring), Op. 12, No. 2 . SCHUMANN . . . | I— | 206 |
| Nachtstück, Op. 23, No. 4 . . . SCHUMANN . . . | I— | 199 |
| Romance in F Sharp, Op. 28, No. 2 . SCHUMANN . . . | IX— | 28 |
| Slumber Song, Op. 124, No. 16 . . SCHUMANN . . . | I— | 202 |
| Träumerei, Op. 15, No. 7 . . . SCHUMANN . . . | I— | 198 |
| Two Grenadiers, The . . . . SCHUMANN . . . | IX— | 182 |
| Warum? (Why?), Op. 12, No. 3 . . SCHUMANN . . . | I— | 212 |
| Scotch Dances (Ecossaisen) . . . BEETHOVEN . . . | I— | 34 |
| Scotch Poem, Op. 31, No. 2 . . . MacDOWELL . . . | II— | 108 |

**Scriabin, A.**
| Nocturne, Op. 9, No. 2 . . . . SCRIABIN . . . | IX— | 52 |
| Prelude, Op. 9, No. 1 . . . . SCRIABIN . . . | IX— | 50 |
| Secret, Le . . . . . . . GAUTIER . . . . | III— | 134 |

**Sentimental Songs.** See Vols. VIII and IX
| Serenade (Les Millions d'Arlequin) . DRIGO . . . . | III— | 61 |
| Serenade . . . . . . . HAYDN . . . . | I— | 71 |
| Serenade (Good Night! Good Night, Beloved!) . . . . . . . NEVIN . . . . | IX— | 208 |
| Serenade . . . . . . . OLSEN . . . . | II— | 128 |
| Serenade . . . . . . . PIERNÉ . . . . | II— | 142 |
| Serenade . . . . . . . SCHUBERT . . . | VIII— | 8 |
| Serenade (Ständchen) . . . . SCHUBERT . . . | I— | 118 |
| Serenade . . . . . . . TITL . . . . | III— | 254 |
| Serenade Badine . . . . . GABRIEL-MARIE . . | III— | 106 |
| Serenade d'Amour . . . . . BLON . . . . | III— | 38 |
| Serenata, La., Op. 3 . . . . HERBERT . . . . | IX— | 115 |
| Serenata, La (Waltzes) . . . . JAXONE . . . . | VI— | 177 |

| | | | VOL. PAGE |
|---|---|---|---|
| Serenata, Op. 15, No. 1 | Moszkowski | | II—118 |
| *Sextette (Lucia di Lammermoor)* | Donizetti | | VII— 48 |
| *Shall We Gather at the River?* | Lowry | | VII—213 |
| *Shall We Meet Beyond the River?* | Rice | | VII—220 |

**Sheherazade**

| | | | |
|---|---|---|---|
| Selection | Rimsky-Korsakow | | IV—220 |
| Shepherd's Dance (Henry VIII) | German | | III—125 |

**Shostakovitch, D.**

| | | | |
|---|---|---|---|
| Prelude in E Flat, Op. 34, No. 19 | Shostakovitch | | IX— 74 |

**Sibelius, J.**

| | | | |
|---|---|---|---|
| Romance, Op. 24, No. 9 | Sibelius | | II—194 |
| Valse Triste, Op. 44 | Sibelius | | II—198 |
| *Siciliana (Cavalleria Rusticana)* | Mascagni | | VII— 22 |
| *Silver Threads Among the Gold* | Danks | | VIII—152 |
| Simple Aveu | Thomé | | III—242 |

**Sinding, Chr.**

| | | | |
|---|---|---|---|
| Rustle of Spring, Op. 32, No. 3 | Sinding | | II—204 |
| Sirens, The (Waltzes) | Waldteufel | | VI— 95 |
| Sizilietta | Blon | | III— 34 |
| Skaters, The (Waltzes) | Waldteufel | | VI— 90 |
| Slavonic Dance, Op. 46, No. 1 | Dvořák | | II— 17 |

**Sleeping Beauty, The (Ballet)**

| | | | |
|---|---|---|---|
| Waltz | Tschaikowsky | | V— 14 |
| Slumber Song | Gounod | | III—162 |
| Slumber Song, Op. 124, No. 16 | Schumann | | I—202 |

**Smetana, Fr.**

| | | | |
|---|---|---|---|
| Bartered Bride (Selection) | Smetana | | IV— 12 |

**Snow-Maiden, The**

| | | | |
|---|---|---|---|
| Selection | Rimsky-Korsakow | | IV—214 |
| Soaring (Aufschwung), Op. 12 | Schumann | | I—206 |
| *Softly Now the Light of Day* | Weber | | VII—222 |
| Solomon Levi | College Song | | VIII—226 |
| *Somebody's Knockin' at Your Door* | Spiritual | | VII—201 |
| *Sometimes I Feel Like a Motherless Child* | Spiritual | | VII—205 |
| Sonata in C (First Movement) | Mozart | | I—128 |
| *Song of India, A (Sadko)* | Rimsky-Korsakow | | VII— 6 |

**Songs for Solo Use.** Vols. VII, VIII and IX

| | | | |
|---|---|---|---|
| *Son of God Goes Forth to War, The* | Cutler | | VII—219 |
| *Song of the Volga Boatmen* | Russian Song | | VIII—155 |
| *Songs My Mother Taught Me* | Dvořák | | VIII— 60 |
| Sorella, La (Two-Step) | Borel-Clerc | | VI—231 |
| Sounds from Home (Slow Waltzes) | Gung'l | | VI—208 |
| Sourire d'Avril (Waltzes) | Depret | | VI—160 |
| Sous la Feuillée | Thomé | | III—246 |

**Southern Songs.** Vols. VIII and IX

| | | | |
|---|---|---|---|
| Souvenir | Drdla | | III— 9 |
| *Spanish Cavalier, The* | Hendrickson | | VIII—232 |
| Spanish Dance, Op. 12, No. 1 | Moszkowski | | II—112 |
| Spanish Dance, Op. 12, No. 2 | Moszkowski | | II—120 |
| Spanish Love (Tango) | Esteban-Marti | | VI—250 |
| Spinning Song, Op. 67, No. 4 | Mendelssohn | | I—173 |

**Spirituals.** See Vol. VII

| | | | |
|---|---|---|---|
| Spring Dance, Op. 38, No. 5 | Grieg | | II— 67 |
| Spring Flowers | Gade | | III— 93 |
| Spring Song, Op. 62, No. 6 | Mendelssohn | | I—178 |
| *Stand Up for Jesus* | Webb | | IX—178 |
| *Stars of the Summer Night* | Woodbury | | VIII—107 |
| *Star Spangled Banner, The* | Smith | | VIII—158 |
| *Steal Away!* | Spiritual | | VII—208 |
| Stephanie (Gavotte) | Czibulka | | III— 56 |
| *Still as the Night* | Bohm | | VIII— 40 |
| Still Waters | Howard | | IX—152 |

**Strauss, Johann and Josef**

| | | | |
|---|---|---|---|
| Pizzicato-Polka | Strauss | | VI— 58 |

**Strauss, Johann**

| | | | |
|---|---|---|---|
| Artist Life (Waltzes) | Strauss | | VI— 21 |
| Blue Danube (Waltzes) | Strauss | | VI— 6 |
| Fledermaus, Die (The Bat) | Strauss | | V—156 |
| Gipsy Baron, The (Selection) | Strauss | | V—166 |
| Morning Journals (Waltzes) | Strauss | | VI— 11 |
| New Vienna (Waltzes) | Strauss | | VI— 36 |
| One Heart, One Mind (Polka Mazurka) | Strauss | | VI— 56 |
| Queen's Lace Handkerchief (Selection) | Strauss | | V—160 |
| Roses from the South (Waltzes) | Strauss | | VI— 16 |
| Tales from the Vienna Woods | Strauss | | VI— 31 |
| Treasure Waltz (Gipsy Baron) | Strauss | | VI— 26 |
| Vienna Blood (Waltzes) | Strauss | | VI— 52 |

| | | | VOL. PAGE |
|---|---|---|---|
| Voices of Spring (Waltzes) | Strauss | | VI— 46 |
| Wine, Women and Song (Waltzes) | Strauss | | VI— 41 |

**Strauss, Richard**

| | | | |
|---|---|---|---|
| *Allerseelen (All Soul's Day)* | Strauss | | IX—188 |
| Träumerei, Op. 9, No. 4 | Strauss | | II—216 |

**Stravinsky, Igor**

| | | | |
|---|---|---|---|
| Firebird, The (Selection) | Stravinsky | | IX— 81 |

**Sullivan, Arthur S.**

| | | | |
|---|---|---|---|
| *Flowers that Bloom in the Spring* (The Mikado) | Sullivan | | VIII—135 |
| Gondoliers (Selection) | Sullivan | | V—250 |
| *Heav'n is My Home* | Sullivan | | VII—238 |
| H. M. S. Pinafore (Selection) | Sullivan | | V—218 |
| *I'm Called Little Buttercup* (Pinafore) | Sullivan | | VIII—138 |
| Iolanthe (Selection) | Sullivan | | V—243 |
| Lost Chord, The | Sullivan | | VII—168 |
| Mikado (Selection) | Sullivan | | V—236 |
| *Onward, Christian Soldiers* | Sullivan | | VII—223 |
| Patience (Selection) | Sullivan | | V—224 |
| Pirates of Penzance (Selection) | Sullivan | | V—210 |
| *Poor Wand'ring One* (Pirates of Penzance) | Sullivan | | VIII—136 |
| Ruddygore (Selection) | Sullivan | | V—229 |
| *Tit-Willow* (Mikado) | Sullivan | | VIII—142 |
| Trial by Jury (Selection) | Sullivan | | V—199 |
| Yeomen of the Guard (Selection) | Sullivan | | V—204 |
| *Sun of My Soul* | Monk | | VII—218 |
| Sunshine and Shadow (Valse Lente) | Henrique | | VI—216 |

**Suppé, Fr. von**

| | | | |
|---|---|---|---|
| Fatinitza (Selection) | Suppé | | V—128 |
| Light Cavalry (Selection) | Suppé | | V—132 |
| Poet and Peasant (Selection) | Suppé | | V—121 |
| *Swallow, The* | Serradell | | VIII—108 |
| Swan, The (Le Cygne) | Saint-Saëns | | II—173 |

**Sylvia (Ballet)**

| | | | |
|---|---|---|---|
| Barcarolle and Valse Lente | Delibes | | V— 73 |
| Pizzicato | Delibes | | V— 78 |
| *Sweet and Low* | Barnby | | VIII—145 |
| Sweet Dream (Reverie) | Tschaikowsky | | III—204 |
| *Sweet Genevieve* | Tucker | | VIII—122 |
| *Sweet Hour of Prayer* | Bradbury | | VII—218 |
| *Swing Low, Sweet Chariot* | Spiritual | | VII—202 |
| Sylphes, Les | Bachman | | III— 24 |
| Sympathie (Waltzes) | Mezzacapo | | VI—172 |
| *Take Me Back to My Boots and Saddle* | Samuels, Whitcup & Powell | | IX—224 |
| Tales from the Vienna Woods (Waltzes) | Strauss | | VI— 31 |

**Tales of Hoffman, The**

| | | | |
|---|---|---|---|
| Selection | Offenbach | | V—184 |
| Tambourin, Le | Rameau | | I— 82 |
| Tango in D | Albeniz | | III— 14 |

**Tannhäuser**

| | | | |
|---|---|---|---|
| Selection | Wagner | | IV—248 |
| Tarantelle, Op. 85 | Heller | | III—170 |
| Tear, A (Un Larme) | Moussorgsky | | III—218 |

**Templeton, Alec**

| | | | |
|---|---|---|---|
| Lullaby, A | Templeton | | IX—122 |
| Mozart Matriculates | Templeton | | IX—120 |
| Tempo di Ballo | Scarlatti | | I— 80 |
| *That Viennese Waltz (A Waltz Dream)* | Strauss | | VIII—127 |
| *There is a Green Hill Far Away* | Gounod | | VII—184 |
| *There is a Happy Land* | Young | | VII—212 |
| *Thine Eyes So Blue* | Lassen | | VIII— 62 |

**Thomas, Ambroise**

| | | | |
|---|---|---|---|
| *Know'st Thou Yonder Land?* (Mignon) | Thomas | | VII— 60 |
| Mignon (Selection) | Thomas | | IV—146 |
| Raymond (Selection) | Thomas | | IV—179 |

**Thomé, Fr.**

| | | | |
|---|---|---|---|
| Andante Religioso | Thomé | | VII—111 |
| L'Extase (Entr'acte) | Thomé | | III—238 |
| Simple Aveu | Thomé | | III—242 |
| Under the Leaves (Sous la Feuillée) | Thomé | | III—246 |
| *Three Fishers Went Sailing* | Hullah | | VIII—151 |
| *Tico-Tico (Samba)* | Abreu | | IX—142 |
| *Tit-Willow (The Mikado)* | Sullivan | | VIII—142 |
| Torchlight Dance (Henry VIII) | German | | III—129 |
| *Toréador et Andalouse* | Rubinstein | | I—213 |
| *Toreador Song (Carmen)* | Bizet | | VII— 16 |
| To Spring, Op. 43, No. 6 | Grieg | | II— 50 |

**Tosti, F. P.**

| | | | |
|---|---|---|---|
| *Beauty's Eyes* | Tosti | | VIII— 30 |
| *Good-Bye* | Tosti | | VIII— 25 |

| | | VOL. PAGE | | | | VOL. PAGE |
|---|---|---|---|---|---|---|
| *Tramp! Tramp! Tramp!* | ROOT | VIII—166 | Lohengrin (Selection) | WAGNER | IV—122 |
| Träumerei, Op. 15, No. 7 | SCHUMANN | I—198 | Mastersingers of Nurnberg (Prize | | |
| Träumerei, Op. 9, No. 4 | STRAUSS | II—216 | Song) | WAGNER | IV—141 |
| | | | Parsifal (Selection) | WAGNER | IV—168 |
| **Traviata, La** | | | Tannhäuser (Selection) | WAGNER | IV—248 |
| Selection | VERDI | IV—236 | Tristan and Isolda (Selection) | WAGNER | IX— 92 |
| Treasure Waltz (Gipsy Baron) | STRAUSS | VI— 26 | Valkyries, The (Selection) | WAGNER | IX— 98 |
| Très-Jolie (Waltzes) | WALDTEUFEL | VI— 76 | *Wait for the Wagon* | BUCKLEY | VIII—121 |
| **Trial by Jury** | | | *Waiting for the Robert E. Lee* | MUIR & GILBERT | IX—231 |
| Selection | SULLIVAN | V—199 | **Waldteufel, Emil** | | |
| **Tristan and Isolda** | | | Always or Never (Waltzes) | WALDTEUFEL | VI— 64 |
| Selection | WAGNER | IX— 92 | Angel of Love (Waltzes) | WALDTEUFEL | VI—100 |
| **Trovatore, Il** | | | Au Revoir (Waltzes) | WALDTEUFEL | VI—109 |
| Selection | VERDI | IV—241 | Dolores (Waltzes) | WALDTEUFEL | VI— 72 |
| | | | España (Waltzes) | WALDTEUFEL | VI— 60 |
| **Trumpeter of Sakkingen, The** | | | Estudiantina (Waltzes) | WALDTEUFEL | VI— 85 |
| *It Was Not So to Be* | NESSLER | V—148 | My Dream (Waltzes) | WALDTEUFEL | VI— 80 |
| **Tschaikowsky, P.** | | | Return of Spring (Waltzes) | WALDTEUFEL | VI—104 |
| Andante Cantabile (Fifth Symphony) | TSCHAIKOWSKY | II—218 | Sirens, The (Waltzes) | WALDTEUFEL | VI— 95 |
| Andante Cantabile (Quartet, Op. 11) | TSCHAIKOWSKY | II—226 | Skaters, The (Waltzes) | WALDTEUFEL | VI— 90 |
| Casse-Noisette (Nutcracker Ballet) | TSCHAIKOWSKY | V— 6 | Très-Jolie (Waltzes) | WALDTEUFEL | VI— 76 |
| Chanson Triste, Op. 40, No. 2 | TSCHAIKOWSKY | III—250 | Violets (Waltzes) | WALDTEUFEL | VI— 68 |
| Chant Sans Paroles, Op. 2, No. 3 | TSCHAIKOWSKY | II—232 | **Waller, Thomas (Fats)** | | |
| Eugene Onègin (Excerpts) | TSCHAIKOWSKY | IV— 84 | Handful of Keys | WALLER | IX—125 |
| Humoreske, Op. 10, No. 2 | TSCHAIKOWSKY | II—248 | Waltz, Cp. 64, No. 1 | CHOPIN | I—149 |
| "June," Barcarolle, Op. 37, No. 6 | TSCHAIKOWSKY | II—240 | Waltz Op. 83, No. 1 | DURAND | III— 72 |
| Melodie, Op. 42, No. 3 | TSCHAIKOWSKY | II—244 | **Waltz Dream, A** | | |
| *Only the Sad of Heart* | TSCHAIKOWSKY | VIII— 18 | *Love's the Tune* | STRAUS | VIII—125 |
| Piano Concerto No. 1, in B Flat Minor, | | | Selection | STRAUS | V—187 |
| Op. 23 (Selection) | TSCHAIKOWSKY | IX— 41 | Waltzes | STRAUS | VI—192 |
| Romance, Op. 5 | TSCHAIKOWSKY | II—235 | Waltzes, Op. 39 (Selected) | BRAHMS | II— 10 |
| Romeo and Juliet (Selection) | TSCHAIKOWSKY | IX— 36 | Waltzes, Op. 54, No. 1 | DVOŘÁK | II— 26 |
| Sleeping Beauty, The | TSCHAIKOWSKY | V— 14 | Waltzes (Selected from Op. 9a) | SCHUBERT | I— 96 |
| Sweet Dream (Reverie) | TSCHAIKOWSKY | III—204 | Waltz in A Minor, Op. 34, No. 2 | CHOPIN | I—144 |
| Valse, Op. 39, No. 8 | TSCHAIKOWSKY | II—252 | *Waltz Song (The Merry Widow)* | LEHAR | VIII—132 |
| *Yes, I Love You (Eugene Onegin)* | TSCHAIKOWSKY | VII— 30 | *Warum? (Why?), Op. 12, No. 3* | SCHUMANN | I—212 |
| Turkish March (Ruins of Athens) | BEETHOVEN | I— 44 | *Watchman, Tell Us of the Night* | MASON | VII—248 |
| Turkish March (Sonata in A) | MOZART | I—124 | Waves of the Danube (Waltzes) | IVANOVICI | VI—168 |
| *Two Grenadiers, The* | SCHUMANN | IX—182 | **Weber, C. M. von** | | |
| Two Minuets (Second Partitur) | BACH | I— 10 | Freischütz, Der (Selection) | WEBER | IV— 68 |
| *Uncle Ned* | FOSTER | VIII—179 | Invitation to the Dance | WEBER | I—160 |
| Under the Leaves (Sous la Feuillée) | THOMÉ | III—246 | Oberon (Selection) | WEBER | IV—204 |
| *Under the Willow She's Sleeping* | FOSTER | VIII—205 | *One Sweetly Solemn Thought* | WEBER | VII—215 |
| Unfinished Symphony (First Movement) | SCHUBERT | I— 91 | Prayer | WEBER | VII—189 |
| **Valkyries, The** | | | *Softly Now the Light of Day* | WEBER | VII—223 |
| Selection | WAGNER | IX— 98 | Wedding March | MENDELSSOHN | I—193 |
| Valse Bleue (Valse Lente) | MARGIS | VI—212 | *We're Tenting To-night* | KITTREDGE | VIII—165 |
| Valse Bluette | DRIGO | III— 68 | *Were You There?* | SPIRITUAL | VII—210 |
| Valse Caprice | FALLA | III— 88 | *What a Friend We Have in Jesus* | CONVERSE | VII—214 |
| Valse Lente, Op. 47 | FIBICH | III— 97 | *When Johnny Comes Marching Home* | GILMORE | VIII—168 |
| Valse, Op. 39, No. 8 | TSCHAIKOWSKY | II—252 | *When the Corn is Waving, Annie Dear* | BLAMPHIN | VIII—116 |
| Valse Serenade | POLDINI | III—224 | *When the Swallows Homeward Fly* | ABT | VIII— 82 |
| Valse Triste, Op. 44 | SIBELIUS | II—198 | *When You and I Were Young, Maggie* | BUTTERFIELD | VIII—172 |
| Valsette | BOROWSKI | III— 46 | *While Shepherds Watched Their Flocks* | TANSUR | VII—216 |
| **Verdi, Giuseppe** | | | *Who is Sylvia?* | SCHUBERT | VIII— 14 |
| *Ah! I Have Sighed to Rest Me (Il* | | | *Who's That Calling?* | SOUTHERN SONG | VIII—175 |
| *Trovatore)* | VERDI | VII— 79 | *Whoopee Ti Yi Yo (Cowboy Song)* | TRADITIONAL | IX—223 |
| Aïda (Selection) | VERDI | IV— 6 | *Why? (Warum?)* | SCHUMANN | I—212 |
| Forza del Destino, La (Selection) | VERDI | IV—112 | **William Tell** | | |
| *Hav'nly Aïda (Aïda)* | VERDI | VII— 10 | Selection | ROSSINI | IV—231 |
| *Home to Our Mountains (Il Trovatore)* | VERDI | VII— 83 | Wine, Women and Song (Waltzes) | STRAUSS | VI— 41 |
| Rigoletto (Selection) | VERDI | IV—208 | Witches' Dance, Op. 17, No. 2 | MacDOWELL | II— 96 |
| Traviata, La (Selection) | VERDI | IV—236 | *Woman Is Fickle (Rigoletto)* | VERDI | VII— 66 |
| Trovatore, Il (Selection) | VERDI | IV—241 | *Work, For the Night is Coming* | MASON | VII—212 |
| *Woman Is Fickle (Rigoletto)* | VERDI | VII— 66 | *Wot Cher!* | INGLE | VIII—110 |
| *Vesti la Giubba (I Pagliacci)* | LEONCAVALLO | VII— 40 | *Would God I Were the Tender Apple* | | |
| Vienna Beauties (Waltzes) | ZIEHRER | VI—164 | *Blossom* | IRISH AIR | VIII— 64 |
| Vienna Blood (Waltzes) | STRAUSS | VI— 52 | *Yankee Doodle* | PATRIOTIC SONG | VIII—157 |
| *Vilia Song (Merry Widow)* | LEHAR | VIII—105 | **Yeomen of the Guard, The** | | |
| **Villi, Le** | | | Selection | SULLIVAN | V—204 |
| Selection | PUCCINI | IV—189 | *Yes, I Love You (Eugene Onègin)* | TSCHAIKOWSKY | VII— 30 |
| Violets (Waltzes) | WALDTEUFEL | VI— 68 | *You Are My Sunshine* | DAVIS & MITCHELL | IX—228 |
| *Vive l'Amour* | COLLEGE SONG | VIII—221 | **Zampa** | | |
| Voices of Spring (Waltzes) | STRAUSS | VI— 46 | Selection | HEROLD | IV— 53 |
| Voice of the Chimes, The | LUIGINI | III—206 | Zingana, La | BOHM | III— 41 |
| **Wagner, Richard** | | | *Zip Coon (Turkey in the Straw)* | SOUTHERN SONG | VIII—180 |
| Bridal March (Lohengrin) | WAGNER | VII—120 | | | |
| *Evening Star (Tannhäuser)* | WAGNER | VII— 63 | | | |
| Flying Dutchman, The (Selection) | WAGNER | IV—152 | | | |